INTERNATIONAL POULTRY LIBRARY

THE SUSSEX & DORKING FOWLS

Silver Dorkings

OTHER TITLES BY Dr. J BATTY

THE
SUSSEX
&
DORKING FOWLS

JOSEPH BATTY

BEECH PUBLISHING HOUSE

First Published 1996

ISBN 1-85736-166-0

BEECH PUBLISHING HOUSE
Station Yard
ELSTED
Midhurst
West Sussex GU29 OJT

Printed in Malta by Interprint Limited

CONTENTS

Early Illustrations of Brown Sussex

PREFACE

The present book started out as a study on Dorkings *only*, in the hope that a new work on this ancient breed would encourage more people to keep them. Although changed quite drastically over the last 150 years they could still be revived and with careful breeding, become a fine table fowl; accordingly, the mission was started.

Before much research had been done it became very clear that the breeds of Sussex and Dorking were so closely linked together that one could not be separated from the other. For instance, in the days of the Sussex and Surrey table fowl commercial activity the breeds taken were Dorkings, Kent Fowl, and the breed now known as Sussex. In fact, these breeds with four toes or five, some with rose combs and others with single combs, all were fattened for the very active London markets. They were reared and fed on the finest foods, with milk added, and produced in vast quantities; many consumers would love to return to the days when free-range table birds, freshly killed and prepared could be available.

Faced with this close overlap the treatment of the breeds had to be modified, thus allowing comparisons to be made, as well as the present-day modifications to be studied. In any event, there had always been an intention to write a book on the Sussex a breed which I was keeping at the time of writing; these were Speckled Sussex, a variety I find quite fascinating.

My thanks are offered to those, past and present, who assisted with the research. The work of the pioneers such as Sir Edward Brown, Harrison Weir, A. J. Falkenstein and others, mentioned in the text, all helped to clarify the development of the breeds. The illustrations by Harrison Weir enabled past developments to be seen. Also his splendid paintings enable the true colours to be seen, even if modified today to some extent ; the Red Dorking especially is now a rare variety so to be able to reproduce it, gives great pleasure. Harrison Weir was not able to record the new Sussex breeds which developed after his death in 1906. Two families have contributed to the continuation of the Dorking in modern times – the Major family and the Oatey's. Modern breeders were also involved with illustrations and Mrs Sally Taylor had photographs of her bantams taken specially.

J Batty, Elsted, August, 1996

Sir Edward Brown
Poultry historian and author who was instrumental in getting the Sussex standardized

A J Falkenstein
Major person responsible for the development of the new varieties of Sussex fowl

Pioneers in the Sussex Poultry development

A NOTE ON THE *COLUMBIAN* CHARACTERISTICS

The colour pattern which features a self–coloured body with black tail (with white or other colour margin on lower feathers), hackle black stripes with colour margin, and wings with broad black edging is known as a 'Columbian' type. The pattern appears to have come from the Light Brahma (for the Light Sussex) and is both attractive and distinctive. It is found in a number of breeds.

Bantams showing what has been termed a super-hackle'. These have been enlarged to show that the desired white edge is rather poor. If carried further the birds will be very like Lakenvelders, a breed with a black hackle.

Columbian Pattern of Feathers found in Light Sussex
See page 48 for examples of faults in Light Sussex

Red Dorkings   (Painted by Harrison Weir)

Old Kent & Sussex Fowl
Painted by Harrison Weir – now an extinct breed.

Silver Grey Dorkings (Painted by Harrison Weir)

Dark (or Coloured) Dorkings
Painted by Harrison Weir. This is believed to be the true colour; many lighter
male versions exist, but this does not allow male and female to match.

Red Sussex (From a painting by Kurt Zander)

Speckled Sussex
From a painting by Kurt Zander.

Buff Sussex Bantams (Courtesy: Mrs Sally Taylor)

Silver Sussex Bantam Hen   Speckled Sussex Bantam Hen
Courtesy: Mrs Sally Taylor

ONE

THE BACKGROUND
& FINDINGS

The history of the two breeds is very much a part of the fabrication of the story of domesticated poultry keeping. Until Victorian times the raising of fowl on farm or smallholding was a means of providing food. The birds were bred for that purpose. With the shows new goals were established which would have far reaching consequences. The interest in these two breeds lies in the fact that one remained a utility breed (the Sussex), whereas the Dorking became a creation of the show era with tragic consequences to its usefulness.

INTRODUCTION

The transformation from Jungle fowl to the many types of poultry took thousands of years*. The various breeds developed along different lines being influenced by the geographical location and the people keeping them. Following the evolutionary forces which operate as a matter of course each breed adapted itself and developed in a direction which allowed it to survive and serve its owner. The latter would select the birds which developed to a required size or laid a sufficient number of eggs; in this way the breeds gradually evolved into those which served the particular community.

Evidence of this fact can be seen when different breeds are studied which come from distinct areas. The main characteristics are present, but there are variations due to geographical separation. Thus it is possible to distinguish quite clearly the Mediterranean types which are primarily layers; they include Leghorns, Anconas, Andalusians and Minorcas. They have similar shape, carriage, temperament, and excellent laying abilities. Yet away from the original

---

* In fact domesticated poultry have been in existence about 4 million years, but records do not exist so far back. For a concise coverage see Keeping Jungle Fowl, J Batty.

environment they vary, whilst they still retain the main characteristics. Thus the Leghorn found in the USA is different from that in Britain, due primarily to the differences in climate, but also to the selection by those who keep them.

Those breeds from Asia of the hard-feathered type are similar to each other. Malays, Aseel, Sumatra Game, Thai Game and others have hard, glossy feathers which are tight fitting and they are very indifferent layers.

Other examples could be given, but enough has been said to explain the differences which exist. The Dorkings and Sussex are both breeds which appear to be natives of Britain or, at any rate, have been in that country from time immemorial and therefore have to be viewed from that aspect.

British Breeds

The *original* fowl of Britain, before the many imports and intermingling of these with the resident fowl, were:

1. Old English Game used for cockfighting, a national sport.
2. Dorkings and similar farmyard fowl such as the Old Kent and Sussex fowl, not yet recognized as standard breeds.
3. Scots Greys and Scots Dumpies in Scotland, said to have a very long history, possibly as long or longer than the Dorking.

Except in the case of the OEG fowl, the birds were kept for eating and, later, for producing eggs. The value of eggs became recognized in the mid-nineteenth century and from that point, with an acceleration in the early twentieth century, great attention was paid to maximizing egg production.

The show boom also started around 1850* so there was an upsurge in interest in standard bred poultry and *standards* were developed by Lewis Wright and others (J Dixon, R Teebay and W B Tegetmeier) which were taken up by the breed societies and the Poultry Club of Great Britain. A similar trend also occurred in the USA and other countries.

In Britain exhibitions generally became popular and poultry breeding received much encouragement from the patronage of Queen Victoria and other influential landowners and citizens. Many new varieties were created from the new breeds that were imported and interbred with the existing breeds.

For a full coverage of the exhibition side see *Art of Faking Exhibition Poultry*, G R Scott, and *Poultry Shows & Exhibiting*, J Batty, available from BPH.

BRITISH POULTRY EVOLUTION

Dorking & farmyard fowl

Old English Game (cockfighting)

Scots Dumpies

Closely related to Dorking but relationship not really understood. Could be missing link in conversion to short legged fowl.

Dorkings & Surrey Fowl

Dorkings recognized from 1876 in stds

Gradually developed into a large bodied, short legged fowl with horizontal body. Other crosses to get new colours and size and shape. OEG, Brahmas and Cochins involved.

Sussex Fowl

Standardized 1903 and later

Utility aspects followed; used for poultry farming. Light Sussex became most popular utility breed. Crossed with Light Brahmas and others to get different varieties.

Kent Fowl

Disappeared as a separate breed (became Sussex).

Possible Development
Discussed in detail in the text.
Further illustrations are also given throughout the text in later chapters.

W B Tegetmeier* an influential breeder, naturalist and writer has shown how breeds of poultry were transformed within a few years to creations that were difficult to recognize from the original imports. The breeds affected were Brahmas, Cochins, Spanish and others that were given exaggerated characteristics (show points) because of the desire to win at the shows. The utility aspects were ignored and birds were produced with large bodies, heavily feathered legs and other features. For example, Old English Game, the pride of the land, became Modern Game, tall and majestic, with very long legs, simply because the judges preferred to see more leg.

Not surprisingly the Dorkings and Sussex were affected by the "craze" that swept the country Both were utility fowl and dual purpose, ie, producing eggs in reasonable numbers and being excellent table fowl which was what they were always designated.

The Transformation

The **Sussex** fowl, not being an exhibition fowl until after 1903 was not affected greatly by the exhibition enthusiasm that was now losing momentum. They continued to be viewed as utility fowl and any changes appeared to consider this aspect. The new colours introduced such as the creation of the Light Sussex by crossing with Light Brahmas, did not reduce the commercial capabilities. Some mistakes were made when attempts were made to increase egg production too far, but these were corrected and even today the breed is regarded as a very useful dual purpose fowl with great potential as a table fowl.

Exactly what happened to the **Dorking** is not clear because many of the methods used by breeders to improve show potential were not recorded. There is evidence to show that the Dorking was a very useful table fowl which was active and would fatten as well as the Sussex. Time and time again breeders in old journals express the suitability of the Dorking as a commercial fowl.

The crossing which took place to improve the body size is also recorded as having taken place around 1850, but affecting mainly the Dark variety and, later, the Silver Grey which was a mutation from the Dark. The shortening of the legs and the more horizontal body seems to have been the reason for the decline. Now they are more difficult to breed and are no longer commercial-type birds.

*Poultry for Table & Market V Fancy Fowl, 3rd ed. 1898.

Bewick Farmyard Fowl

Thomas Bewick (1753 – 1828) was a wood engraver noted for his accuracy of his engravings of country matters.

Old English Game Fowl

The usefulness for which it was renowned has gone and in its place there is a fowl which cannot possibly be commercially viable because it no longer has the attribute for foraging and activity needed to breed. Indian Game suffer from the same problem and are show birds only.

The change can be seen from study of illustrations of birds over a period of time; the drawing of the farmyard fowl by Bewick around 1800 and other records. Thus the evidence is as follows:

    1. Bewick fowl.
    2. Old English Game Fowl before being transformed into a Modern Game.
    3. Dorkings drawn around 1850 before the legs became very short and the carriage became horizontal.

This shape and shortness is rarely seen in any other breed for the simple reason that it is not a normal characteristic of the useful bird. The main breed with very short legs is the Scots Dumpie and this is genetically known as a "Creeper", no doubt due to the way it walks. Japanese bantams also have this gene, but with a different body. The unfortunate breeding problem with the creeper is that a large proportion die in the shell, due to a lethal gene. The remainder are made up of two-thirds creeper and the balance normal. If the Scots Dumpie was used to produce the shorter legs and horizontal carriage then this could be at least part of the problem of the Dorking for breeding and for viability.*

Unfortunately, there is no proof that the Scots Dumpie was used except that which is circumstantial. There is the fact of the transformation from a fairly upright (normal) fowl to one which has short legs and has a horizontal carriage; there is the lack of foraging ability and the very slow maturity, and finally there are pictorial records to show that the top breeder (A J Major) also kept Scots Dumpies.

The Dorking may not be the true Creeper, but it certainly has the attributes of this type of fowl which is a separate breed in the USA. Compared side-by-side there is no mistaking the relationship.

---

* I am not alone in considering the possibility of the breed being related to the Creeper. See *Bantam Breeding & Genetics*, Fred P Jeffrey. He states that Creepers produce 25% with long legs, 50% with short legs and 25% dead in shell because of very short legs. The same author also states that "in some ways the creeper resembles the Dorking". He also confirms that Scots Dumpies have the same short-legged genetic factor as found in Creepers and Japanese bantams. This phenomenon is not limited to poultry: Dexter cows which have short legs have the same problem - see *Poultry Breeding*, G E Mann, HMSO, 1953.

Seventeenth Century Shape
(F Barlow 1626 – 1702)

Bewick Fowl

Present Day Dorking

Scots Dumpie

Dorkings around 1850.

Ideal Shape

Silhouettes of Fowl to show changes in Shape
Not to scale

Dorking Standards

The evidence, which will be discussed in greater detail in the chapters which follow, indicates that the Dorking and Sussex were originally from a common stock. Both were utility breeds with medium size legs and fairly upright bodies. For the Dorking, the British *Standard* states: **moderately long back with full saddle inclined downwards to the tail.** This occurred in the earlier birds but is not present in the present-day, horizontal bird which does not have a sloping back. The tail of the male should be carried at an angle of 45 degrees and should be large and full. (USA *Standards*). The modern bird tends to have a shorter tail carried at a lower angle, reflecting the shape of the carriage.

Originally then there was close affinity between the two breeds, but the later changes have widened the gap. The Dorking is still a magnificent fowl, but has lost its utility aspects and therefore it is now purely a show bird. There is nothing wrong with this fact as such, but it does seem a great shame that the usefulness for which it was renowned has been lost.

The **consistency of the standards** and the types of birds which exist in practice are open to question. Why should some varieties be different from others? The Darks and Silver Greys are larger than the other colours. In some, the comb is single, in others rose. Even when single combs are being considered there is no consistency in size. Also the carriage is more upright in the Whites and Reds and positively horizontal in Darks and Silver Greys. This *hodge podge* has no place in proper *standards*. Either they are wrong or the birds being bred are not in line with the requirements. The nature of a breed is that it should be capable of being bred on a consistent basis; this is not being achieved in Dorkings between the different varieties.

Sussex Standards

There is greater consistency with the standards for the Sussex. However, even here there are some variations between the colours. The Light has been developed to a high level of perfection possibly because such large numbers have been bred. In others, for example, the Silvers, tend to have longer backs, and the Speckled vary in colour. Possibly in time, with more interest being shown in the rare colours, the position will improve. In the British *standards* the "short" legs and thighs should be qualified – this is the same as for the Dorking, which is patently untrue when comparisons are made.

TWO

BACKGROUND :
THE 'SUSSEX' AS A
TYPE OF TABLE FOWL

The 'Sussex fowl' description originally referred to a type of table bird which was produced by farmers in a district of Sussex from the sixteenth century.** There were also 'Surrey fowls' which were similar. In fact, Dorkings, Sussex and similar type-fowl existed for hundreds of years and were not standardized being selected purely on the basis of ability to fatten well and possessing ample white flesh and white legs. The Sussex breed really came into a recognizable form around 1904 when it began to be shown.

Introduction

Although a reasonable layer*, the Sussex Fowl is regarded primarily as a **table breed;** that is, one bred and managed with meat production as the main objective. Indeed, at one time it epitomized all that was foremost in producing high class chickens for the market to supply hotels, restaurants, and other consumers. Around the breed grew the "Sussex Chicken Industry", which supplied fattened chickens to the London markets, being taken by horse drawn wagons three times each week. This was even before the development of the railways and the consequent improvement in transport.

The art of fattening was a specialized skill handed down from father to son (or daughter), and great care was exercised to make sure that the birds put on weight rapidly within a specified period (usually 16 weeks). Run properly the farm would make a profit, but if side tracked there was a danger that the birds would be given too much food and would not be ready at the optimum time.

* This general assertion may be challenged by some, especially when the Laying Tests are considered; more than 250 eggs per annum have been recorded.
**See *Sussex Methods of Table Poultry Production*, John H Dowden, World's Poultry Congress paper in 1927. The 16th century has not been authenticated, but the Poulters' Company was given a Royal Charter in 1504.

Various methods were used for cramming – giving a plentiful supply of food so the flesh would be developed at the desired rate. It was found that by careful feeding in limited–space accommodation the birds would grow to almost twice the size in the same period.

They were as follows:

1. **Hand Feeding of Pellets which is labour intensive. The operator takes a prepared pellet and dips it in whey and then inserts it into the mouth of the bird whilst the beak is opened.**
2. **Feeding through a Funnel using a liquid in the form of a cream. The funnel is inserted into the gullet and the crop is filled. It is very effective.**
3. **Using A Cramming Machine which allows an experienced operator to feed 250 birds per hour. This is the most effective method.**

Fattening by use of hoppers whilst the birds are in cages is not strictly 'cramming' which implies force feeding in some form, although it is part of the fattening process.

These days we would frown on the methods used, although, in reality, they were probably better than those used for commercial egg laying when three or four hens are placed in a small cage. The forced–feeding was the unacceptable face of the industry. Using a special machine, with a pipe which was inserted into the beak of a bird, food was 'pumped' in, until the crop was quite full.

Despite the harshness of some of the methods it must be appreciated that on the whole the conditions were quite good. The main features were as follows:

1. **Eggs were collected or purchased and hatched under broody hens; incubators came later.**
2. **The hens were allowed to rear batches of chicks.**
3. **Specialization developed so that one class of farmer would hatch and rear the chicks and another class would 'finish' them by adding extra weight in a period from 12 to 16 weeks of age.**
4. **The birds would be fattened, killed and plucked, then put into boxes which maximized the market appeal.**

The special methods of feeding were developed over hundreds of years. No grain was given because it was discovered that wet mash developed the crop to its maximum size, thus facilitating the fattening process. An added advantage was the fact that the Sussex–type food resulted in more tender and succulent meat. There has to be continuous growth from start to finish and at the final cramming the skilled operator knew exactly how much food could be given to maximize the fattening process.

Area of Location

The area in which the rearing and fattening took place was in Sussex in the district of Heathfield. The area consisted of some 75,000 acres and there were around 1,500 small farmers involved, many with about 50 acres. It consisted of Heathfield, Horeham Road, Warbleton, Dallington, Brightling, Burwash, Mayfield, Rotherfield, Buxted, Uckfield, Framfield, Waldren, East Hoathly, Chiddingly, Laughton, Ripe, and Chalvington.

The climate of the district is thought to have influenced the growth of the industry. It has a wide main valley, thickly wooded ridges, deep cut lanes and plenty of shelter. There was also access to the two collecting points for transporting to the London markets; first by horse and cart and then by Rail.

The chicks were reared primarily by use of broody hens which were cooped in open fields. Accordingly, they had to be very hardy. At between 12 and 16 weeks of age they would be transferred to the fatteners, being collected by a person known as a higgler who was a middleman. From then on, for three or four weeks, they would be subjected to special fattening treatment by experts.

A disadvantage was the fact that six of the parishes concerned had to contend with Wealden clay, which made rearing of poultry more difficult. Only the skill of the farmers and the strong constitution of the birds made the venture possible.

However, around 1903 the breed was fast disappearing and Edward Brown commented on this fact at a meeting of farmers he addressed in that year.* As a result, in July 1903, a Sussex Poultry Club was formed and the breed was revived and given formal recognition.

From a Government report, **Report of the Royal Commission on Agriculture,** 1895, it would appear that the "Sussex" had already disappeared from the scene by around 1880. The report laments the loss, commenting that the Sussex was the 'almost perfect' table bird, with white legs, heavy body and broad breast.

Yet the provision of high quality birds had been profitable and thriving. Techniques for fattening, cramming, killing and dressing in an attractive way were all part of the industry. The birds commanded high prices, but high quality was essential.

---

*It would appear that the farmers took umbrage at the suggestion that the fowl were being neglected and forgotten; so they decided to have the well established breed recognized.

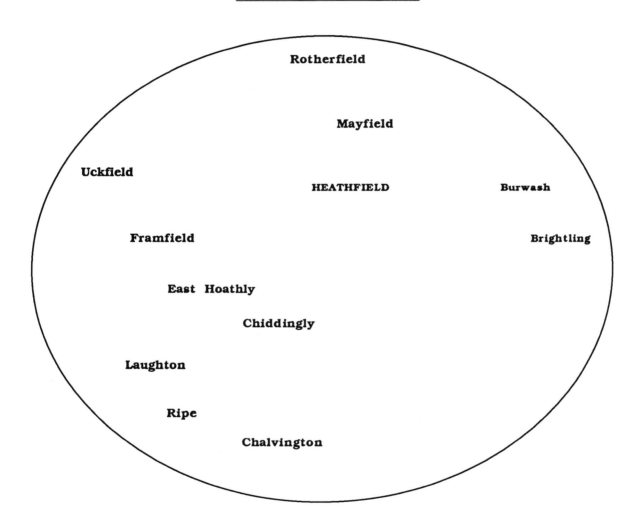

ROYAL TUNBRIDGE WELLS

Rotherfield

Mayfield

Uckfield

HEATHFIELD   Burwash

Framfield   Brightling

East Hoathly

Chiddingly

Laughton

Ripe

Chalvington

<u>EASTBOURNE</u>

The Sussex Fowl Industry Location
Approximate Location of main Places (see text)

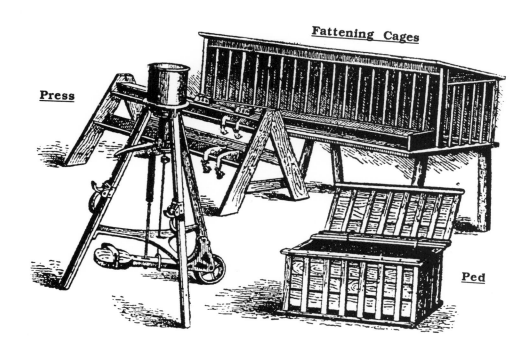

Fattening Cages

Press

Ped

Fattening Cages

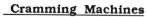

Cramming Machines

The Fattening Process
For further details see pages 15 & 16

The Decline

With the war of 1914 – 1918 the industry went into decline and never recovered. Other uses were found for the land and the farmers looked for other opportunities such as dairy farming which offered more scope at the time. However, a revival took place and the Light Sussex continued to be kept and became the top bird for laying and table. The other varieties also gained from the popularity of the Light variety.

There was a 'revolution' in farming methods and poultry farming became a large scale operation. Instead of special, high quality birds the **broiler** was developed, a fowl which would fatten very quickly, could be killed and (at a later period in time) could be frozen exactly when ready for eating, and could be made available cheaply. The introduction of deep litter and other types of production methods allowed thousands of birds to be reared and fattened under intensive conditions. The era of the chicken as an every day meal had arrived.

Improvements in food technology went a long way towards the **super chicken**; high levels of protein and various chemical additives, measured out in exact percentages, meant that birds could be got ready within definite periods so that contracts could be agreed upon where batches of birds would be ready for killing at the time agreed.

Great strides were made and the industry boomed, but the birds used were 'hybrids', cross breeds which were bred specially for the purpose. Unfortunately, in the rapid growth and developments some of the quality was lost. Reports of meat **tasting like cardboard** were the result and producers had to look for ways and means of giving better birds.

The broiler appears to have come to stay because this intensive rearing is the only way that low prices can be achieved. However, there is a positive movement for the supply of 'free range' birds and who knows when the Sussex might come back into its own again for those who want a bird which is fed on natural foods and is of a high quality. It must be appreciated that in the heyday of the Sussex poultry industry the birds were reared in a most exacting way.

The food was 'natural' in the sense of not having chemical additives. Attention was paid to high quality ingredients which were fed at optimum times.   *Attention to detail appears to have been the secret of the successs achieved, but these were the days of long hours and low wages so labour costs were low.*

MENUS USED

The food given to the birds was selected to give the necessary rate of growth and, at the end of the period, meat which was tender and tasty. If birds could be run on grass before fattening this was an added advantage, but the birds so reared were a luxury item, intended for the gourmet market, where high prices could be obtained to earn a profit.

Procedures Followed

A typical method of fattening was as follows:

The birds should be fed in the troughs twice daily; the trough being removed when sufficient food has been consumed....

The food consisted of a mixture of Sussex ground oats (in fact, this was a *composite* mixture of eight sacks of oats to one of barley), milk and fat.

The oats should be ground in the Sussex manner (the millstones being "dressed" very fine with a sharp pointed handpick), otherwise the meal will not be sufficiently fine, and the unground piece of husk, so common in other meals, are liable to cause digestive derangements. (putting in the whole husk and grain was recognized as being desirable for the best results).

The milk (usually skimmed) was allowed to go sour before use. Sometimes mutton fat was melted and mixed with the meal up to 0.50 oz per bird daily.*

The food is initially mixed so that it is almost "pourable", then after a week it should be thickened into a crumbly state. Do not overfeed, but keep the appetites sharp. This takes place over two weeks by which time the birds should be killed or crammed for 7 days by hand or by use of a cramming machine. Again, the purpose is to put a finish on the birds and not go on too long or the effect will be spoilt. Great skill is required to know exactly the optimum time for fattening.**

This represents a summary of the main features of the system. In practice there were variations, but the basic approach was the same; to grow quickly and then add extra weight in a coop or by cramming. It was expected that 1lb. would be added to a cockerel in 10 days.

---

* Many years ago I had access to a supply of batter scraps from the local fish and chip shop and found that these mixed with layers' meal fattened up the cockerels at a very fast rate. (Author)

**A summary of the procedures from *The Encyclopedia of Poultry*, J Stephen Hicks, London, 1921. It is interesting to note that the author had a poultry farm at Heathfield, Sussex, the centre of the fattening industry.

OTHER FEATURES OF THE SYSTEM

There was little merit in fattening birds to a point of excellence only to be spoilt because of poor marketing, including presentation. The rules followed were:

1. Peak Weight to be Achieved and then Kill.
The skilled fattener knows when to stop fattening at the point when further feeding will be uneconomic. The bird is then killed by dislocating (pulling) the neck. Under the Sussex system there was no starving beforehand because there was no delay to get them to market.

2. Preparation – Press to Shape.
The birds would be plucked and stubs taken out before the bird is cold – the sooner the better. They are then placed in a press which is an arrangement of shelves in which birds are placed breast downwards and then heavily weighted to get the correct shape.

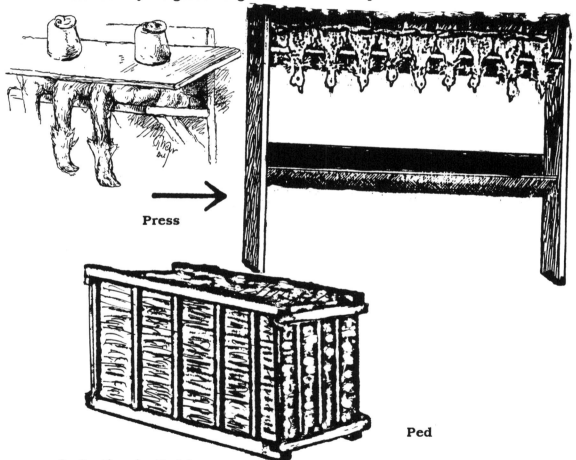

Press

Ped

3. Crating in 'Peds'.
Once cold, the birds are placed in special crates known as Peds which are slatted to allow for adequate ventilation. Clean wheat straw is place between each layer of birds.

Once in the peds and labelled they would be speedily sent to market so no delays occurred at any time in the preparation and delivery.

THREE

ORIGIN
OF THE SUSSEX
&
LINKS WITH THE DORKING

As noted in Chapter 1, the Sussex as a standard bred fowl was first seen in 1903/4 and it is from this period that the utility fowl in a definite form began to appear. This chapter examines the origins and offers a review of its development.

The Ancient Origins

The **Sussex-type** of fowl either came with the Romans in 55 BC or they were here when the invasion took place in some other form, which was similar to the Dorking and the Southern breeds of poultry. The link with the original Dorking fowl must have been very close*. Various writers have referred to a five-toed breed which is a layer and table bird. However, the extra toe characteristic is not of itself evidence that the breed was always so endowed, although this seems likely.

Undoubtedly there has always been a strong link between the Dorking and the Sussex. At one time it seems that the latter was regarded as a Dorking with four toes. If this is correct they enjoy the same antiquity and come from the same parent stock. The earlier recognition of the Dorking came from the fact that the breed was established from an early date and, as a result, Dorkings were shown from 1894 in the USA and at the first shows in the UK.

The possible relationship with **Scottish breeds** should not be overlooked. The Scots Grey is believed to be related to the Dorking

---

*Wm Cook in *The Practical Poultry Breeder & Feeder*, asserts quite positively that the Sussex were originated from the Light Brahma crossed with Buff Cochins, into which some Silver Grey Dorking was introduced. In the *modified form* of some of the colours this may be true, but Cook also admits the ancient lineage of the Sussex-type of fowl (this pre-dated the entry of Brahmas and Cochins into this country about 1850).

and the Old English Game fowl.   Certainly, the colour of plumage and the legs and flesh, being white, would indicate common ancestry. On the size and shape the possible link theory falls down. However, considering the OEG cross the argument becomes feasible and even the absence of the fifth toe is explainable, because, over time this would be bred out. As noted by Edward Brown, at one time there was a tendency for Scots Greys to be Dorking type and the plumage is similar to the Cuckoo Dorking.*

On possible safer ground, but certainly more controversial is that the Scots Dumpy is related to the Dorking. In fact, since there have been suggestions that the breed was taken to Scotland by the Phoenicians before the Roman invasion it may even be possible that the Dorkings were larger versions of the Dumpies, improved in size by selection. We have only to look at the breed and see the resemblance in shape and carriage.

They were listed at the very first poultry shows (1852) and records indicate a very long history. It is said that the Dumpy was a *time-keeping cock* (presumably like the long crowing fowl of China and Japan)**, as well as being "watch dogs" in times of war; they are always alert and will give the alarm when there are sounds in the distance. The Romans found they could not approach the encampment of Scots or Picts without the alarm being set up by the Dumpies.*

In more modern times it is remarkable that the foremost breeder of Dorkings in the country (A J Major) was also the breeder of Scots Dumpies which won first prizes at major shows in England and Scotland.

Today the Scots Dumpy might be a possible candidate for reproducing both large and bantam Cuckoo Dorkings to ensure this beautiful variety continues. They are around half the weight of a top weight Dorking.

The Literature on Poultry Breeds
The early references to breeds of poultry show the ancient lineage of the Dorking and its relative the Sussex fowl. Unfortunately, with all things ancient, evidence must be circumstantial, gleaned

---

* Edward Brown, *Poultry Breeding & Production,* London, 1929.
** J Batty, *Japanese Long-Tailed Fowl,* Midhurst, England 1994

SCOTS GREYS.

SCOTS DUMPIES.

The Scottish Breeds
These may have a link with the Dorking

from existing writings, with assumptions being made on the likely explanations.

The most likely conclusion appears to be that the Dorking (or "Darking" as it is also called in earlier literature) came with the Romans and was not present in Britain before their conquest. The circumstantial evidence is based on the works of Roman writers who described the breed. Thus there is Columella, who wrote on agricultural matters prior to AD 47 when he died and who states:

> **The best fowl should be: "reddish or dark plumage, and with dark wings......The breeding hens should be "of a choice colour, a robust body, square built, full breasted, with large heads, with upright and bright red combs .... those are best with five toes."**

He therefore knew of a 'Dark' Dorking (or possibly the Red) and from another part of his writing he had experience with the White, because he believed they were not as productive as the darker variety.

The other main Roman writer, Pliny, in his work *Historia Naturalis,* (AD 77) states that:

> **Superiority of breed in hens is denoted by an upright comb, sometimes double, black wings, ruddy visage, and an odd number of toes."**

It will be noted that there was reference to a rose combed variety (double) and to the fact that the number of toes was unusual.

Other early writers have commented on the Dorking:

1. M de Reaumur, *The Art of Hatching and Bringing Up Domestic Poultry*, Paris, 1751
He commented on the fifth toe not being very useful, but expressed the opinion that the breed was large and should be kept.

2. Bonington Moubray, *A Practical Treaty on Domestic Poultry*, London, 1815
This book gave the first description of the breed as known today. Presumably the town which may have given the breed its name, was originally known as 'Darking' for this is the name he uses or it may be a mis-spelling. However, as Edward

Brown *(Poultry Breeding & Production, London, 1929)* points out, the breed was to be found in other parts of the country, not only the south, but also in Cumbria and parts of Scotland. The same author (Brown) also asserts that the Dorking type was bred extensively in the Weald of Sussex. Therefore the name Dorking may not be conclusive for establishing that the breed originated from Dorking. The **Darking** name may refer to the colour and not the place.

Turning back to Moubray it should be noted that he believed that they were named after the town where "probably the variety was first bred".

There appears to be no proof either way. What is certain is the fact that birds of a similar type were bred and fattened in Sussex and this provides the definite link with the utility fowl which were later (1904) to be named Sussex.

3. Wingfield W and Johnson G W., *The Poultry Book*, London, 1853
These are important authors who brought together facts relating to the breeds of poultry in the 1850s when the poultry show boom was starting.

4. G Ferguson, *Rare and Prize Poultry*, London, 1854
Ferguson believed there was evidence to show that the Dorking had been bred in the Dorking town area and its environments from 1683. He does not supply evidence of this statement, but we cannot give a basis for contradiction. Even if accepted, and there is no reason to doubt Ferguson, there is a gap of around 1,700 years, when the Romans left Britain. But the observations of **Harrison Weir** on the poultry markets (below) are relevant to this issue.

5. Lewis Wm M , *The People's Practical Poultry Book*, New York, 1871.
The work by Lewis is interesting because it comes from the USA where there was great interest in poultry and regular transportation of birds between the two countries. The illustrations demonstrate the shape and form before they were modified for show purposes. He refers to them as the "Surrey Dorkings" and the fact that, originally, (he believed) these were best if white in colour.

6. Arthur Roland. *Poultry Farming* , London, 1879.

Roland regarded the Dorking as the best fowl to keep. His observations are therefore of great merit. He also quoted John Baily one of the early English writers on poultry, including the Dorking, in a treatise entitled "Management and Fattening of the Dorking Fowl".

The fact that the Dorking has been used to cross with other fowl (presumably to get a faster growing type) as well as to introduce new blood and to overcome the effects of inbreeding, has caused much confusion. His opinion was that the cock had to be changed each year because, unlike the Old English Game, it did not possess the vigour of the latter.

The single comb was attributed to the crossing which had taken place, because the rose comb and five toes belong to the *pure* Dorking. Any fowl not having the five toes is not a Dorking being the result of a cross with the fowl of Sussex, Surrey or Kent.

As a table fowl Dorkings are unequalled, being cooped for fattening at 3 or 4 months of age. This process takes around 16 to 20 days. They are fed corn, and oats mixed with milk.

Dorkings are not renowned for foraging*; accordingly, they must be well fed and they will then respond and lay reasonably well.

They make excellent broodies, but should not be used to hatch and rear chicks from small, delicate breeds.

7. Sir Edward Brown, *Races of Domestic Poultry* **and** *Poultry Breeding & Production,* both listed and referred to throughout this book.

As noted there are differences of opinion on which is the best colour; no doubt the strain plays a part in the opinions expressed. However, some are smaller than others and some possess more bone and therefore may better to be avoided.

---

* Differences of opinion exist on this characteristic. Some have suggested that Dorkings are not active, but other breeders state that the breed will do well on free range at one time used to be seen working the home fields. See Wm W Broomhead, *Poultry Breeding & Management*, London,

White Dorking Cock

Pair of Grey Dorkings

Illustrations of Early Dorkings
Source: *The People's Practical Poultry Book*, Lewis
Note the difference in shape from the later illustrations

Other writers should be noted, such as Harrison Weir *(Our Poultry)* and Lewis Wright *(The Book of Poultry)*. Both gave their views at around the turn of the century.

Lewis Wright re–affirms the Roman origin of the Dorking*, expressing the view that the Romans occupying the British Isles were fond of poultry meat. On the Sussex breed he expressed the hope that the old Surrey and Sussex fowl would be revived. He was of the opinion that the Sussex had a part in creating the coloured Dorkings. He believed the Sussex was unique in its 'width and flatness of back' and surpassed the Dorking in this respect.

Here then is a view that the Sussex was a separate breed which existed as a distinct utility fowl.

Harrison Weir gives some clue to the earlier reference by Ferguson on the antiquity of poultry breeds. From early times poultry was sold in London: 1345 a patent was granted by Edward III to deal in poultry and it was ordained that the fowl should be sold at "Leaden-hall" and nowhere else. The Poulters' Company was founded in 1504 by Royal Charter and various acts were passed renewing the charter by different monarchs. He grouped the pure English farmyard stock together, lamenting at the crosses with Cochins and Brahmas. Accordingly, he appears to regard the Sussex as a sub–variety of the Dorking.

Obviously much has changed, but street names still exist in London to show what went on, including the use of the name *"Poultry"* to this very day.

Market Requirements

The provision of birds for the market was undoubtedly the main purpose of the poultry trade and the **Sussex or Surrey fowl** were produced for that purpose. As noted, this description referred to a type of table fowl and not to a specific breed.

---

* The Roman origins, cited at greater length earlier, appear to be fairly conclusive. However, as stressed, the evidence on the Dorking of today being the same breed (with some modifications) as that kept by the Romans is quite circumstantial. Most authorities agree that the Dorking is an ancient breed, but one author is of the opinion that the story that the breed was brought over by Caesar and his Romans is as well authenticated as that of Alfred burning the cakes. He admits its long history, but doubts the precise nature of the early origins. (*The Truth About Poultry*, G R Scott, London, nd). Fortunately, this is a minority view.

A farmer, named Henry Lane of Wokingham in Berkshire, specialized in providing Dorkings to Leadenhall market and he had a
reputation for top quality birds which fetched high prices (£1 per
pair is quoted). His system described by R W Webster (*Management
of Poultry for Profit,* London, 1899) is as follows:

1. Dark Dorkings were found to reach heavy weights.
2. A cock and 10 hens were run free range.
3. Bred from mature hens (2 or 3 years old).
4. Marketed annually 250 birds.
5. Cockerels and pullets were reared together until 6 months then
separated for fattening.
6. Cramming was not practised because the natural method was better.
7. The food was finely ground barley meal, coarse suet and skimmed
milk. For 20 fowls it required two gallons of meal, one pound of fat and
three quarts of milk. Maize meal and coarse sugar or treacle were added
occasionally for variety.
8. The fattening took place in coops with food placed in troughs at the
front, along with water. This took 3 weeks to finish off the birds. The
birds were expected to reach 7 lb. for cockerels and one pound less for
pullets.

This was a profitable business and continued for many years.
Except for the avoidance of cramming it followed the standard pattern.

Sussex Fowl Ready for the Market

The Poultry Press

The early references to breeds in the magazines published give guidance on what was occurring. In the journal *The Poultry Review* for 20th December, 1873, the breeds shown at the Lewes and County of Sussex Show were as follows:

**Dorkings; Brahmas; Cochins; Hamburghs;
Spanish; Polish; Game; Any Variety**

The 'Any Variety' class was for those exhibitors residing in the County of Sussex. In fact, the breeds mentioned as winners were Malays, Silkies, and Andalusians, There was no mention of Sussex fowl which is not surprising since they were recognized as a separate standard breed only from 1904, stated earlier.

MODIFICATIONS TO THE BREED

The discussion on whether the Dorkings and Sussex are related and to what degree must also consider any major crosses which have taken place in one breed or the other. According to one eminent writer (W B Tegetmeier, *Poultry for Table and Market versus Fancy Fowl,* 3rd Edition, 1898, London) and confirmed by research from others (eg, H Easom Smith, *Modern Poultry Development,* Liss) the true Dorking was changed dramatically and to its detriment by Mr John Douglas, poultry keeper to the Duke of Newcastle, who crossed the original Dorking with a Malay–type bird (a large Dark Grey Kulm) probably obtained from the Zoological Gardens (some sources suggest the bird came from a ship which had returned from India). This bird weighed 13 lb. and he was placed with seven hens and the offspring were all Dorking type birds which achieved large weights over 10 lb. and one cock over 14 lb.

According to Tegetmeier the result of the increase in size was a "degree of coarseness, loss of table qualities, and by greatly increased size of bone, particularly in the shanks". This increase in bone, which became the aim of exhibitors to win prizes, resulted in a larger frame, with a deterioration in the quality of the breed as a table fowl. The exhibition requirements were out of line with table needs; size of bone and beauty of plumage became the first considerations. Accordingly, "In place of the very compact, short legged, fine boned breed of 20 years ago, characterized generally by speckled plumage, we now have exhibited a much larger breed....".

The colours were also changed because the Dark Grey influence spread to most of the birds being kept. The Cuckoo or Blue Dorking went out of fashion because, according to Tegetmeier, they did not reach the size required for exhibition. They were noted as layers and were excellent table birds, with juicy flesh; they also matured early which made them suitable for the market.

In the *Journal of Horticulture* dated 25th August, 1881, Mr O E Cresswell a noted breeder stated:

> **The Dorking was formerly a more uniformly square-shaped, short-legged, round, deep breasted, and white footed bird than it is now. When exhibitions became frequent breeders found that the judges of poultry gave great weight to size and weight in Dorkings; indeed, at the Birmingham Show, they used to weigh them and in spite of the well known rule about purity of breed, &c. being rather taken into account 'than mere weight', seemed to ignore many of the old points.**

This aspect is also discussed under the section dealing with **colours**

The crossing which took place in producing different breeds also had an influence on the question of the relationship of the Sussex and Dorking. For example, the Dorking was used in the production of the Buff Orpington and then the latter was involved in the development of the Buff Sussex. Other crosses occurred, some of which are no longer on record, so we can never be sure on the exact relationship, especially when dealing with the colours which were introduced long ago. Old English Game would certainly have played some part in introducing new colours because in that breed there are all possible colours available; also they have no unusual features to eliminate after a cross has been made.

---

* The later Dorkings were bred back to the original strain and therefore some of the "ill effects" noted by Tegetmeier would have been reduced in intensity. What occurred with this breed has been a normal practice to improve breeds and emphasize points or features; we cannot therefore suggest that Dorkings were markedly different from other exhibition stock. Other breeds also suffer from the inconsistencies, for instance, Wyandottes and Orpingtons, but with Dorkings the variations in size, shape, weight and comb are quite great for a breed of such antiquity, and steps to improve should be made so all comply with a set standard.

Acceptance of the New Strain

The new strain, produced by John Douglas, proved to be very popular and from 1858 was taken up by many exhibitors. At the Crystal Palace Show in 1870 the Cuckoos and Reds were relegated to the AOV classes; the main colours being exhibited were Coloured (74), Silver Grey (41) and White (14), a total entry of 129.

The Birmingham Show around that time had 305 entries in eight classes. The prize winners included many landowners and gentry. Duke, Duchess, Countess, and other titles all featured. Possibly the decline in the breed could be linked with the declining fortunes of these great households where the provision of poultry meat would be an important culinary requirement? In 1914, details in the next chapter, the total number at the Crystal Palace Show was 131, which was still a large turnout. In 1924, despite the 1914–18 war, the Club Show had a total of 150 entries. Yet by 1936 the breed was losing out rapidly to the newer breeds; it must also be appreciated that the Poultry Industry was now being re-developed for mass production so a bird which was an indifferent layer and slow to fatten would not be a first choice. The Sussex possessed the necessary qualities that allowed the exhibition and utility features to be combined so it did not suffer to the same extent.

Writing in 1927, George Scott (*Modern Poultry-Keeping*) laments the virtual disappearance of the Dorking due to: "Lack of robustness....delicacy of the chickens, and the absence of any exceptional attainments in the way of laying..". The same author stated that the Sussex had out-distanced the majority of its competitors; its utility properties has ensured that the breed had a wide following.

Influence of Physical Characteristics and Colours

Before any conclusions can be reached on the degree of relationship which exists between the two breeds it is necessary to examine in more detail the following:

1. **Characteristics of make up as described in the** *standards*;
2. **The colours that exist and those that existed in the past, particularly in the early stages.**

These are the subject of later chapters.

FOUR

PHYSICAL CHARACTERISTICS

The Overall Shape & Confirmation

The shape of the two breeds as they exist today can be seen from the illustrations given overleaf. In brief the following apply:

1. The Sussex

This is an orthodox shape with the body oval and long in shape and with a full breast, which should be well covered in flesh, being broad and plump. The legs and thighs are moderately long when compared with the Dorking. The British standard suggests *short* thighs and shanks and the American *medium*, which is more accurate.

The plumage is fairly close so the shape can be seen without difficulty. The head, neck, and tail are all of moderate size or length. In the male the tail should be set at 45° and in the female 35°. The comb is single and upright.

The standard type has four toes which is quite different from the Dorking, which has five toes, a characteristic present from very early times. The egg is tinted to brown in colour.

2. The Dorking

The Dorking has many general features like the Sussex, but there are also marked differences. The body is long, but it is also low. It is also inclined to be at an angle with the slope towards the tail.

The tail is set at the same angle as the Sussex, but in fact appears lower because the front and back of the body are longer than the Sussex.

The legs are quite short and the thighs, also short and stout, are hidden with the profusion of feathers under the breast. The presence

Cont. p. 33

Comparison of the Shapes
Sussex

Definition of a Dorking
(T W Sturges*, *The Poultry Manual*)

Male

The general characteristic of the Dorking should be their great size and weight, the deep, square body, with a long and prominent breast bone, white skin, short white legs, and white feet, which should be long and well spread out, and with their chief characteristic, the five toes, the fifth being distinctly apart from the fourth, and, after leaving the shank at a right angle, is turned upwards. Great stress is placed upon the feet, both in colour and shape. The bone should be finely rounded and hard in quality, not soft and spongy, as otherwise the bird soon develops lameness. The head is large and wattles are large and pendulous, the comb large, circular in arch, evenly serrated in the single comb variety; viz, Dark, Silver or Red. The rose comb is found on the White, Cuckoo, and also in the Dark Dorking. It should be square in front, moderate in size, the top covered with fine nodules, and the peak at the back inclined slightly upwards. The eye should be full and large, with a bright red or yellow iris in all varieties.

Female

The general characteristics of the hen are somewhat similar to those of the cock, allowing for difference of sex. The single comb in the hen is fairly large, and should fall gracefully over to one side of the face. The body is long, deep, and massive, the back level, broad across the cushion, and tightly feathered. The tail is well developed with broad feathers, and carried closely, not fan shape. The carriage is staid and matronly.

This definition should be studied very carefully because it contains all the main features of the Dorking. These are elaborated further in the book. Is should be apparent that size and shape are very important and colour is secondary, although when birds are judged within a specific colour class it must be taken into account.

The reader will appreciate that the varieties do differ, not all being the same size or the same shape, although the overall impression should follow the description given. The modifications which took place did increase the weight of the Dark and Silver Greys, but the remainder were not affected and are more like the original form of Dorking.

*Past President, Poultry   Club of Great Britain

Overall, staid and graceful

Body rectangular in shape & deep; carriage horizontal

Comparison of the Shapes
Dorking

Comb large with hen's falling over one side

Neck hackle tended towards 'bull-neck'

Rosecomb: Whites & Cuckoos

Short, white legs with five toes

Comparison of the Shapes

of the fifth toe has been noted. Without this special appendage there can be no Dorking; this must be on white legs.

The long and massive frame is also an essential requirement and any hint of tallness must invalidate any claim to be a Dorking.

Other Features to Compare

The other features which should be compared are as follows:

1. Head and Comb

The Dorking tends to have a wider head and hackle. As a result the wattles of the Sussex appear more set back and are not as long as the Dorking. Ear lobes are medium in size.

The comb of the Sussex is single, whereas the Dorking can be single or rose, depending on colour. The rose is in whites and cuckoo.

2. Egg Production

As noted, the Dorking lays a white egg and is not usually regarded as a good layer; the Sussex is a better layer and the eggs tend to be brownish – they vary in depth of colour, from tinted to brown.

SUMMARY OF DIFFERENCES

The main differences to be found between the two breeds are as indicated above and for convenience are now summarized:

1. Body

Dorking has a sloping body with a deep keel; the Sussex have a deep, broad body with a flat back.

2. Legs

Legs must be pinky white, but in the Dorking there is a fifth toe.

3. Colours

This aspect is considered in subsequent chapters. The question to ask is whether the colours in both breeds are compatible. However, this is also linked to the matter of how the specific sub-varieties were produced.

The leg colour indicates a common ancestor, but the body exhibits considerable variation. Taken over a very long period this may be a case of separate development in different areas. Charles Darwin showed there can be considerable variation even when descended from the same ancestors. Pigeons in their many varieties came from the Blue Rock dove. Poultry came from the Jungle Fowl.

The ability of the Sussex to develop and fatten much quicker than the Dorking is an indication that the two breeds are different*. The rate of growth can be affected by food, but the appropriate genes must be present or the birds will not develop at a fast rate. It has been established that rate of growth is inherited. A cross with a slower growing type of breed would also affect the fattening ability and the Douglas cross described in the preceding chapter indicates that this took place. If the cock in question was a "Malay-type" and on this there is no absolute proof, and different claims are made by Tegetmeier and Lewis Wright, then certainly the Asian breed would give greater size, but slowness in maturiity.

The Fifth Toe (Known as "Polydactyly")

The unusual and, some assert, useless fifth toe is a characteristic which has caused discussion. Occasionally the extra toe appears on the Sussex, but generally speaking it has four toes.

That it serves no purpose has to be accepted for a fowl has no need for the extra toe. W B Tegetmeier (*Poultry for the Table & Market, etc.*) states the position as follows:

> It is needless to say that the extra toe, which is supposed to be an indispensible characteristic of the true Dorking, is a considerable drawback from a utilitarian point of view. It is an unquestionable deformity, the presence of which often leads to lameness and bumble foot. Although the modern show Dorking is not adapted to the producer of fowls for the table, it may, by judicious crossing, lead to the production of cross breeds of considerable value.

The disparaging remarks on the unsuitability of the **modern show Dorking** was a reference to the cross made by John Douglas around 1850, to produce larger, heavier boned birds, covered in more detail elsewhere.

The question as to why the fifth toe has continued, is given consideration by the remarks of Professor R C Punnet (*Mendelism*, London, 1911). He addressed the question in his chapter on Dominance:

> In certain breeds of poultry such as Dorkings there occurs an extra toe directed backward like the halux. In some families this character behaves as an ordinary dominant to the normal, giving the expected 3 to 1 ratio in F2. But in other families similarly bred the proportions of birds with and without the extra toe appear to be unusual. It has been shown that in such a family some of the birds without the extra toe may, nevertheless, transmit the peculiarity when mated with birds be-

---

*The influence of what has been termed "hybrid vigour" would apply because the Sussex varieties (including the successful Light Sussex) were developed from crossing with other breeds.

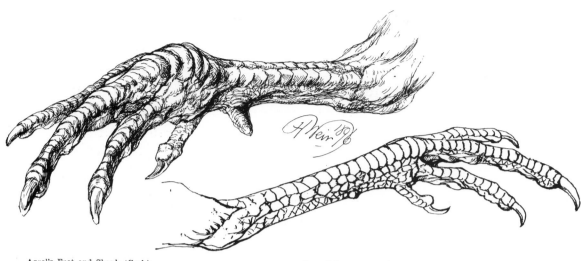

Azcel's Foot and Shank (Cock).
Owned by Author.

Leg of Game crossed by Game Dorking Hen.
Bred by Author.

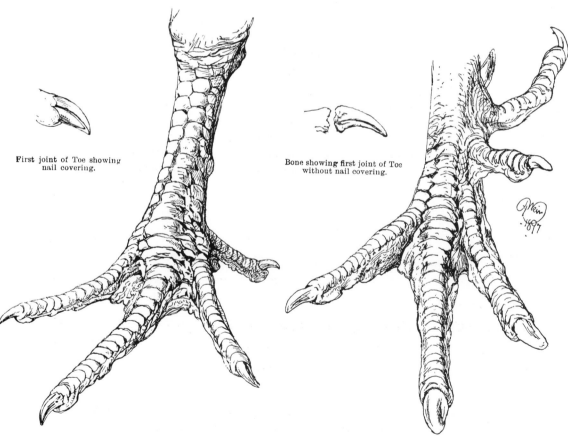

First joint of Toe showing
nail covering.

Bone showing first joint of Toe
without nail covering.

Leg of Surrey or Sussex Fowl (Cockerel).
Pure white and white Toe-nails ; Fore Toe same length as Shank ; Side
Toe as long as the Middle Toe, to end joint ; Hind Toe just has the
length of Side Toe ; Out Toe 4, Middle 3, Inner, 2 joints

Front View of Tawny Old Kent Hen's Leg.
(Observe the breadth of Toe-nail.)

The Feet & Legs including the Fifth Toe (Drawn by Harrison Weir)

longing to strains in which the extra toe never occurred.

Interestingly, the other breeds which have the extra toe, the Silkie, Faverolles and Houdan, are quite different from the Dorking and two are from different origins; the Faverolles is said to have been produced from crossing with Dorking, Houdan and Cochin. Various researchers have tried to explain the reason for the inheritance of polydactyly. They came to the conclusion that its presence was due to a dominant autosomal gene; however, in four toed birds there were other genes which inhibited the inheritance of the fifth toe. (See *Poultry Breeding*, Morley A Jull, NY & London, 1947)

Whether the feature is an abnormality is open to debate. Its existence in the two very old breeds of Dorking and Silkie, as well as the French breed the Houdan, indicates a long history. Admittedly, as far as we know, the Jungle Fowl has never possessed five toes, but there is no recorded history of very early domesticated fowl. Possibly the extra back toe was for gripping; before birds could fly did they climb by means of three toes at the front and two at the back? We are not likely to know, but it is hard to believe that an extra toe just appeared for no purpose. If viewed from today's requirements the fifth toe is superfluous, but it should not be dismissed as a freak occurrence.

For the purpose of this study we are concerned with whether the Dorking and Sussex are related in a modern context or whether they are the same breed in a different form. They appear to have been developed separately and authorities like Harrison Weir have recorded the existence of breeds of poultry in Sussex and Kent which are different from the Dorking.

The conclusion must be that they are a separate breed, but closely related. Bearing in mind the relative newness of the recognition of different breeds, this is the only approach feasible because all breeds are related in some way and treating the Sussex differently from others could not be justified. Agreed the Sussex was not recognized until 1903, but then a breed which was probably the Dorking, which was mentioned in very early literature, back to Roman times, was not given **official recognition** until 1865 in Britain and 1874 in the USA.

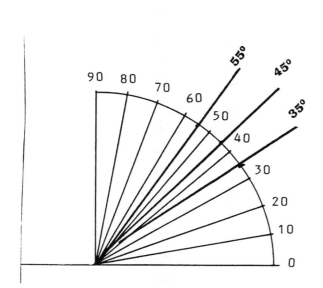

Tail Measurement Diagram
(Degrees)

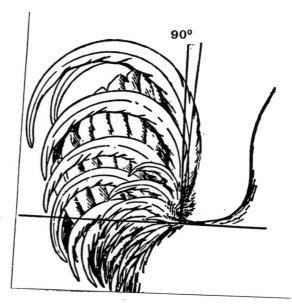

Squirrel Tail
(A major fault)

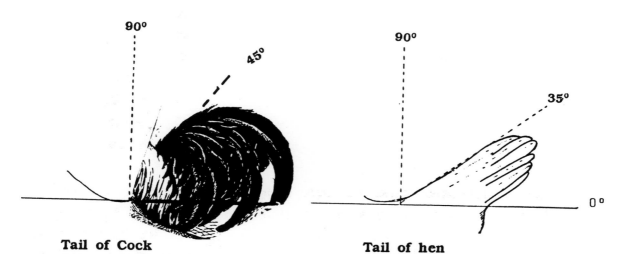

Tail of Cock

Tail of hen

Expect Dorking to be much fuller and back to be more horizontal which affects the appearance of the tail.

Comparison of the Tails

The angle is indicated, but this must be viewed in relation to the slope of the back. The USA standard states 45° for males and 35° for females in both breeds, but the Dorking tail is wider and fuller than the Sussex. In practice some variation of 5° is allowed, but it must be apparent that the modern Dorking male has an angle of about 30°, which is incorrect.

SIGNIFICANT DEVELOPMENTS

The breeds have been developed and improved over a considerable period and it is useful to consider the most significant stages in the popularity of the breeds. Today the Light Sussex is still very popular in large and bantams, but the development of hybrids and the growth of the bantam fancy has reduced the numbers of the Dorkings and Sussex quite drastically. Yet these breeds are very much the answer to the return to free range systems; they are hardy and productive and can stand the rigours of the British and similar climates.

The Pre-1914 Period

The period immediately prior to the Great War is significant because this was an era of normality when farmers and fanciers kept poultry as an everyday event without the problems of feeding and before the youthful population were called up.

Sussex

Referring to table poultry W Henfrey (*The Poultry World Annual, 1914*) commented on the excellent display by the Sussex breed. The leading exhibitor was F H Wheeler, President of the Table Poultry Club. In this connection Sussex received the most mention with Dorkings only linked with cross bred birds (Indian Game X Dorkings), which made excellent table birds.

A Fine Champion Speckled Sussex Pullet
Winner of many firsts, including Crystal Palace and Lewes; F H Wheeler

The Exhibition Side – Sussex

On the normal show side, reported in *The Feathered World Year Book,* 1914, there was mention of results at Haywards Heath, Dairy, and other shows. The colours given special mention were Red, Light, and Speckled. The latter was very popular, but there was difficulty in getting the birds to breed an even shade of colour.

Results for 1913 (summarized)

Manchester	Palace	Birmingham
Red Ckl 16; Pullet 16	Red Male* 28; Female* 20	Brown Male 11
Light Ckl 18; Pullet 21	Light Male 23 ; Female 45	Brown Female 14
Speckled Ckl 25; Pullet 28	Speckled Male 42; Female 29	AOC Male 13
Brown Ckl 10; Pullet 15	Brown Male 12; Female 15	AOC Female 10
	(Special Brown Club Show)	

* Ckl and Cock combined and hen and pullet combined.

Dorkings

A well known fancier Clem Watson, reported, (*Feathered World Year Book,* 1915) that:

The good old Dorking is a long way from being dead. At some shows they seem to fall off, but at the great classical events of the year they keep up their reputation.

Leading exhibitors were A C Major and H C Douglas. Whites were very scarce, yet they were apparently an original colour.

Results for 1913 (Summarized)

Dairy	Palace (Club Show)
Coloured Ckl 16; Pullet 15	Col'd Male* 29 Female* 25
Silver Grey Ckl 9; Pullet 10	Silver Grey Male 21; Female 23
----------------	Mixed: Novice Male 14; Female 19

* Ckl and Cock combined and hen and pullet combined.

The Manchester Show had no classes and at Birmingham there was a total turnout of 43 birds in mixed varieties.

Champion Red Sussex   (Major J A Morrison)

Champion Brown Sussex Hen (Charles Hardy)
Typical Sussex in the 1924 Period

The 1925 Period

This was a prolific period for Sussex when the Sussex Club Show had more than 500 entries for 1924. In this period Clem Watson reported:

1. Light Sussex
This variety was the most popular and at the Dairy Show there were 330 entries and this included 109 Light pullets.
2. Browns
These were in reasonable numbers.
3. Speckled
Satisfactory, but appeared to be on the decline.
4. Reds
Good turnout.
5. Browns
Not a strong turnout.
6. Buffs
Struggling to survive.

Colours were being understood better so fanciers were more interested and more classes were being offered at shows.

Dorkings

Unfortunately, the decline in popularity had already started. It was reported in *The Feathered World Year Book* for 1924 that the breed was losing ground because the "craze is all for layers". Entries at major shows were:

Club Show 150 entries of very good quality exhibits.

Dairy Show 38 entries compared with 51 in 1923.

Position in 1936

Around this time there was more awareness that the **Sussex** breed should not be changed too much towards being a 'layer' with large eggs. This was desirable, but not at the expense of losing 'type'. In the 1930s the Light variety continued to be kept in larger numbers and they did well at the Laying Tests.

The Dorking continued to lose support and, although a number of colours were present, many were in small numbers. The Whites and Cuckoos were quite scarce. The Red was being revived and the

Silver Grey and Dark were low, but not in danger.

An Overall View

The overall trend has been for the two breeds to move in opposite directions. The Sussex, particularly the Light variety, has continued to be kept in substantial numbers.

Unfortunately, the **Dorking** in all its colours, as indicated above, has become quite scarce and is no longer kept as a utility fowl, being regarded as a show bird only or one kept out of interest in a true British breed. Even then the Silver Grey tends to be the colour normally seen.

Numbers being exhibited in the **Sussex** were variable with figures in the region of 50 to around 100 at the major shows. In the 1980s and onwards the numbers at the Club Shows were around 40 for large, and bantams came in around 150; later turnouts continue in a similar pattern. The colours are Light, Speckled, Buff and White (large) and the bantams have also Silvers. However, the Light Sussex bantams are by far the most popular.

The interest has been in a utility breed which would lay large, tinted eggs and to this end there was considerable interest in the laying trials. The utility clubs used to be popular and the Scientific Poultry Breeders Association (now discontinued) had many members who kept Sussex

Dorkings continue to struggle for support. The numbers at the Rare Poultry Society show tend to be around a handful in Darks and Silver Greys. The Club show attracts reasonable numbers for a minority breed. A typical good year is around 35 birds. However, many members do not exhibit so show numbers in themselves are not always a true indication of interest in a breed and its numbers. At the time of writing there are 100 members who keep around 600 birds. Half of this number are Silver Greys and 15 per cent Darks. The remainder are Reds and Whites with the Cuckoos in the low minority.

A few dedicated fanciers often make all the difference to a Club or the advancement of a breed. A C Major and A J Major of Ditton, Langley, Bucks dominated the breed for very many years. Birds from the latter breeder were photographed for posterity and can be seen in old books and journals. Another is the Oatey family which have kept the breed for 100 years, through four generations and still serve the breed through the Club.

COMMENTS ON MANAGEMENT

Management requires sound accommodation and a sheltered position for the run. Here it is necessary to note any special requirements for the breeds and varieties. As will now be obvious, the Dorking, from being the main breed, has declined and is now kept only by a dedicated few. Various reasons have been advanced for the loss in favour:

1. The Fifth Toe
In the standard form, the toe grows quite long and becomes an impediment.* In addition, the breed was inclined to become lame and develop a problem known as bumble foot.**

2. Chicks are Delicate
It is necessary to breed with unrelated birds and then give the chicks plenty of room for rearing. They may suffer cramp during the first six weeks although this can be avoided by rearing them on soft scratching material.* Very early chicks are best avoided; April is early enough and May is better for success.**
It will be appreciated that this was written before the introduction of modern chick crumbs which make rearing much easier.

3. Not Able to Stand Heavy Soils or Harsh Conditions.
Many authors make this point. They require a dry, well drained soil and an extensive range. Otherwise they may suffer from consumptive catarrh.**

4. Indifferent Layers
There is no denying that they are primarily table birds. However, when a *selected pen of layers are put together they cannot be regarded as bad layers.*

On the other hand, many breeders swear by their merits and there is little doubt that with proper management, with modern foods, they can be profitable when viewed as a dual purpose fowl. As stated by Wm Cook, possibly the most famous of practical poultry men, commenting on their merits:

They have a long, deep breast, and are of fine flavour, their meat being of very fine texture. The Dorking fowl will never die out as long as England stands.

These are strong words from an expert poultry breeder. If more breeders take them up – and what better now free range is being thought of in realistic terms, then the Dorking can be improved because they will not be so inbred.

---

*Wm Cook, *Practical Poultry Breeder & Feeder* , St Mary Cray, various dates.
** M A Wilson, *Poultry Book*, London, nd.

Breeding Problems

There are no special breeding problems in achieving the standard colours. At one time it was suggested that double mating (having one pen for breeding pullets and another for cockerels) was essential for the Reds, but this seems no longer essential. Breeeders experienced with Dorkings have come down in favour of avoiding double mating and this is in accordance with modern views.

The Sussex

The Sussex, particularly the Light variety, being a composite breed, and inclined to be very active, has replaced the Dorking as the premier dual purpose fowl. It suffers from none of the problems outlined above for the Dorking. Any criticism has been levelled at some strains which have been bred for egg production and, in the process, have lost the ability to reach the weight and size desired. In addition, again with some only, the size of egg has suffered (below 2 oz.) and the number laid has not been at a high level.

The exact reason for the popularity of the Sussex is hard to pinpoint. There was the decline of the Black Orpington which became largely a show bird – yet originally had been a very high producer. According to George R Scott (*The Truth About Poultry*) there were other contenders for a top breed, but the Sussex was given the crown. Thus:

> Why precisely, a breed, ancient as any this country has produced, and for generations unknown outside the marches of the county which gave the breed its name, should suddenly leap into vast popularity it is impossible to say with any exactness. Undoubtedly, this Sussex is one of the best general purpose fowls extant, unquestionably it deserves full and widest recognition.

...With the boom in the Light Sussex :

> The Speckled, the Red, the Brown, have all found considerable support, though it is supremely doubtful if they will ever climb the heights reached by the Light.

There are no problems in breeding for standard colours, although the colour of the hackle may have become too black with insufficient lacing in some specimens. The chicks can be bred early, thus getting the desired growth early in the year. If heavy breeds are hatched in March they make the best Winter layers. Sussex are hardy birds and will thrive on free range with an output of around 150 eggs.

Light Sussex Bantams   Silver Sussex Bantam Cockerel

Dorking Bantams
Drawing to indicate type in bantams.

Bantams
In type should follow the large breed, but 25 per cent of size.

BANTAMS*
Sussex

Bantams exist in both breeds, but the Light Sussex is the most popular. The size is for the male around 40 oz. (1130 g.) and 28 oz. for female (British) and the American 36 oz and 30 oz, respectively for the cock and hen.

Very fine specimens of a number of colours are seen at shows. On the Light Sussex some judges have expressed the view that too much emphasis has been given to the hackle markings; undoubtedly, these have improved in the last decade and a bird with a washed out hackle will never win. However, the question might be raised on whether some are now too dark, being almost black. The black centre should be surrounded by a white margin, but this is becoming rather difficult to see on some specimens. The Columbian-type plumage is a feature of the Sussex breeds (except White and Cuckoo which do not appear to exist in bantams) and is best seen in Light Sussex (see page viii).

More attention should be given to size and type which should be more important than the hackle. There is a tendency for birds to be over-size and this should be penalized as should any other faults such as rose comb. feathered legs, five toes and faulty plumage. This is not to say that heavy breed bantams should be diminutive. If too small, lacking the width and depth of the large equivalent, reduced in proportion, they cannot be regarded as true miniatures of the large breed.*

Colours are discussed in the chapter dealing with that aspect.

Dorkings

They have never been a popular breed as bantams, because they are difficult to bantamise. As noted, in connection with Sussex, the bantam should be in proportion to the large breed and this is being achieved with the Sussex. Regretfully, the following for Dorking bantams is much smaller so there is not the same effort possible. In fact, many of the bantams, which tend to be the Silver Grey variety, are not typical of Dorkings when viewed as miniatures of the large fowl**.

---

* A theme expanded at length by Dr W Clive Carefoot in "Some Thoughts on Heavy Breed Bantams" in *Poultry Club Yearbook* for 1984
** Many modern bantams are too upright and long in the legs with the result that we have to look twice before deciding the breed, possibly on the basis of the colour. There appears to be some Old English Game bantam in the make-up.

FIVE

THE STANDARD COLOURS

The Colours

Writers on poultry breeds assert that **the shape decrees the breed and the colour the variety** and there is much truth in this statement. However, it is only a *tendency* and should not be taken too literally. Some breeds have only one colour and therefore without that colour there can be no standard breed; the Ancona and Andalusians are examples. Another factor is that different colours in a breed may have slightly different characteristics, depending on the original make-up of the parent stock. It has been shown that the **Dorkings** had a cross in the 1850s which changed the shape and size, but not all colours were affected in the same way. In **Sussex** there are differences between the Light and the Speckled and, since various breeds were used to produce the former, such as Dorking, Brahma and Cochin, the differences are still present, although over many years of breeding since the cross, the Light has emerged as a standard bred fowl of a clear Sussex type.

Sussex Colours

The standard colours are as follows:

1. Brown;	**2. Buff;**
3. Light;	**4. Red;**
5. Speckled;	**5. Silver;**
6. White.	**7. Cuckoo (not standardized, but said to be an original colour)** [*Feathered World Yearbook*, 1928, R Terrot]

In the USA the Light, Red and Speckled are recognized. Other odd colours have existed, but have generally disappeared when the

Examples of Faults in Light Sussex

The Light Sussex is a "Columbian-type" bird which means cock's *head and back* silvery white; *hackle* black with narrow lacing of white; *tail* black; *wings* white with black lower edge of primaries; *breast* white; *body* feathers white; *legs and toes* white. The hen is white with hackle black, with white lacing and tail black.

breeder concerned lost his enthusiasm. A noted example is the Blue Sussex which is still around although not standardized; in 1937 there was a Coronation Sussex, similar to the Light, but with lavender or blue-grey neck and saddle hackles.

Light Sussex*

The Light Sussex is the main variety and should be white with neck hackles striped a prominent black. The black is also seen in the flights when the wing is opened and the tail is black.

The earlier types had a rather washed-out black in the hackle, but this no longer occurs; the *standard* stipulates that the black stripe at the black centre of the hackle feather must be enclosed within a distinct white border.

The **plumage faults:** are stripe running out of the feathers **(D in drawing)**; white shafting **(C)**; black markings on cape and saddle feathers; smutty under colour; white in tail; ticks or marks of black, yellow, rust, or grey on body.

Examples of Faults in Light Sussex

The faults which may be found on typical birds are as follows (See Drawing Examples of Faults in Light Sussex):

1. Cockerel 1:
(a) High breast with cut-away front (bad)
(b) Thigh too long
(c) Poor, weak tail - sickles and coverts too narrow

2. Hen 2:
(a) Poor front and tail
(c) Breast poor indicating unlikely table bird

3. Cock 3:
(a) Stocky but back too short
(b) Tail not at correct angle
(c) Breast not developed
(d) large comb; (e) Excessive fluff around abdomen and thighs.

4. Hen 4:
(a) Short in stature
(b) Head heavy
(c) Tail short and stubby
(d) Cushion too feathery

Breast
A and B; Short breast in A unacceptable; B long, level breast is correct
Plumage C, D & E. E is correct; C and D faulty - see text.

*The colour was first produced from crossing Sussex/ Silver grey Dorking with Light Brahmas, thus getting the typical Columbian-type plumage.

Brown Sussex

These follow the Black-Red pattern, the male having a mahogany hackle, back and saddle, and a black breast and tail. The females are brown with black stripes in the hackle and a breast which is a wheaten brown; black 'peppering' appears on the back. This variety was said to be rather large in body and excellent layers of brown eggs, although for a time it was said to be the smallest of the varieties.*

This variety was first introduced in 1908-9, but the original Sussex Club refused to give it recognition. As a result, a Brown Sussex Club was formed to cater for its needs. The dispute was on the basis that the original Club felt that there was already sufficient colours in existence.

This new variety was in effect a Black Red cock and Wheaten hen and some felt that the description "Brown" was not really appropriate.

Buff Sussex

The overall colour is an even, dark golden buff with the neck hackle and tail as for the Light Sussex. The creation of the colour was said to be due to a cross with the Buff Orpington*. It was introduced after 1918 and there were difficulties in getting the correct shade and the black hackles. Since the Buff Orpington was produced by crossing a Golden Hamburgh cock with a Dark Dorking and then the pullets were mated to a Buff Cochin cock it can be seen that the Dorking blood is in the Buff Sussex.

Red Sussex

Reds should be a deep rich shade with the hackle striped black. Tail black and under colour is slate. This colour is one of the original varieties and is not a composite breed like the Light. It is a similar shade to the well known Rhode Island Red, although not such deep chocolate (more reddy), but with the typical striping of the hackle in black; the tail is black and the wings have black in the flights. This is a very handsome fowl of typical Sussex markings.

---

* Edward Brown, *Poultry Breeding & Production*, London, 1929

Speckled Sussex

The Speckled claims to be the *original* Sussex. According to Edward Brown, when the Sussex Poultry Club was formed in 1903, the variety was regarded as the most typical and more numerous than others. Unfortunately, they varied a great deal in colour and in producing exhibition birds the utility quality was lost.

According to Mr Clem Watson the Speckled should be as follows:

> Each feather on a Speckled male should have a clean white spot at the tip, then a broad bar of glossy black, the rest of the feathers being rich dark mahogany. The under-colour should be slate and red with a minimum of white, and the flights in both male and female white, brown and black. The tail of the hen should be black and brown with a white tip, whilst in the cock the main tail feathers should be black and white, and the sickle feathers black with white tips.
>
> The wing bow in the cock should be speckled (ie, a mixture of brown and white feathers) and the neck and saddle hackle feathers rich dark mahogany striped with black* and tipped with white. In the females the rich dark mahogany colour is most essential and yet it is most difficult to obtain, because with the black bar dividing the white from the red there is always the tendency for the main part of the feather to show black or peppery marking.

(From *Sussex Fowls*, Clem Watson, London, 1926)

Although of ancient origin there are some who believe that the Speckled *colour* originally came from the Old English Game Fowl and then the OEG characteristics bred out.

In earlier times they were known as Old Kent **Spangles** and this accords with the description of the colour found in OEG today. Then they were called Spangled Sussex and finally were re-named Speckled Sussex. Since the Old English Game are just as old or older than the Dorkings and the old Kent Fowl, it would not be surprising that at some stage OEG have been used to give more vigour to the breed.

The OEG Spangle and Speckled Sussex are very similar in the pattern and type of spangles; however, generally the Speckled Sussex are darker in colour, a burgundy being present for male and female (Partridge in OEG). An extra colour gene is responsible++.

---

*Because of the "speckle", the stripe is not as obvious as in the Light and other varieties. ++ See *Concise Poultry Colour Guide*, J Batty, 1996.

There is a tendency for Speckled to go rather light in colour with age, and white feathers extend in wings and tail. However, some strains appear too dark and are not large enough in size.

The Speckled is a most attractive colour, but sadly is not kept on a large scale, although there are still some around and letters on the breed have been received from as far away as Australia. Only a coloured illustration can do justice to the rich colour and markings of the variety. A coloured plate, based on a painting by A J Simpson and issued by The *Feathered World*, shows the beauty of this fascinating and useful colour and is worthy of study. It will be noted that the breed does not have the *obvious* striped hackle of the Light, Red, Brown, Red and Buff, although it is present.

The Silver Sussex

This colour is rather like the 'Grey' in Old English Game with a black body and hackle, saddle and back a silvery white; the hackle has a black stripe on each feather. There is also lacing on the breast, although not all breeders believe this is essential.

The White Sussex

There were high hopes of this variety being very popular. However, a pure white variety amongst so many attractive colours did not seem a sound notion. In 1936 a Mr F J Marston wrote an article (*Feathered World Year Book*) on the variety, noting that it conformed more accurately to the 'Sussex type' than the Light Sussex.

In the laying tests they performed well with an average of 218 eggs per bird and of the total eggs produced (2,406) only 23 were second grade. The weights achieved were also quite good.

The main criticism of the breed was the excess feathering which tended to delay maturity in the growing bird. Colour must be pure white. A number of authorities* have stated that the White Sussex started life as a new breed known as the "Albion" and then became the White Orpington. However, this view does not agree with the account given for White Orpingtons by Wm. Cook who developed the breed and, certainly, there is a wide variation in shape between the two breeds. The Falkenstein Whites were quite different. The continued inclusion in the *British Standards* appears to be optimistic, although some do keep them.

SUSSEX BANTAMS

The colours listed are also recognized in bantams. In the USA there are Buff, Birchen (presumably the same as the British Silvers), Dark Brown, Light, Red, Speckled, and White. In Britain the Lights are very popular and most other colours are being bred.

---

* See for example: *Poultry Breeding & Management,* **Wm. W Broomhead, London,** © **1938**

Coronation Sussex – Blue Hackles & Tail
A new breed produced by H Whitley in 1937 (not standardized)

Cuckoo Sussex
This is similar to the Cuckoo Dorking in barring

Dorking Colours

Like many of the other breeds with a number of colours the Dorking has seen many changes, depending very much on the fashion at the time. The *British Standards* recognize:

1. **Cuckoo**   2. **Dark (Also known as** *Coloured*)
3. **Red**   4. **Silver Grey**
5. **White**

The USA *standards* stipulate White, Silver Grey and Coloured. (Darks) They were admitted to the American **standards** in 1874.

In the Cuckoo and White the comb must be of the rose type. In the Darks (British) the rose **or** single comb is allowed, but in the American Coloured it must be single. In the Silver Grey and Red the comb is single.

In reality, in Britain, the two colours seen are the Silver Greys and Darks. Cuckoos are very rarely seen and Reds are rare.

The colours, except for Whites, do tend to show some variation, which is allowed. The shape, size and pure white feet are very important.

Cuckoo Dorkings (Barred)

Dark grey or blue barring on light blue–grey background, the colours shading into each other. In short it is rather like the well known Barred Rock or Scots Grey. They are seldom seen and according to many writers were always difficult to breed to a standard colour. In fact, double mating may have been necessary.*

It is recognized that the **bars should not be sharply defined at the edges, like the Hamburghs, but should shade into the lighter tint of the ground colour, and the bars of pencilling are broader and coarser than in pencilled Hamburghs.****

They may have been produced from a cross with the American Dominique. However, the influence of the Scots Dumpie or Scots Grey should not be overlooked and the former seems more likely.

Leading breeders in the early part of the 20th century were the Countess of Dartmouth and Lady Aylesford.

---

* Editor of the *Stock-keeper*, 29th July, 1892.
** L C R Norris-Elye, *The Poultry Book*, London, nd.

<u>Dark or Coloured Dorkings*</u>

The Dark **male** has a black breast and under parts. The hackles yellowish straw striped with black; the back is a mixture of colours grey, black and white with maroon intermingled; wing bows straw to darkish maroon, possibly with white, mixed with grey or black with a glossy black bar across the middle. Wing feathers, secondaries, black inner web and white outer, primaries, black or dark slate.

The **hen** is salmon- to browny red on the breast, each feather tipped with a dark grey verging on black. The tail is black and the remainder of her plumage is a rich, dark brown approaching black, each feather slightly pale on the edges and showing a dull white stripe (shaft) in the centre. In practice, **a second type** is found with body feathers which have pencilling. The hackle is certainly dark as shown on the Harrison Weir illustration shown earlier, but can vary to an almost black colour with a straw margin on each feather.

They are very similar in colour to the Silver Grey, but are darker (including burgundy or maroon) and tend to be larger in size because of the new blood introduced. The Silver Greys appear to be pure in colour, whereas the Darks do vary more in terms of markings and density of shade. The "purity" is based simply on selection for the silver-grey colour which is a straightforward process.**

Another possible source of the Silver Grey colour was a cross between Whites and Partridge Cochins. It is said that a Mr Fisher Hobbs was responsible and the information was handed down by word of mouth by Harrison Weir to Joseph Pettipher, a noted breeder and junior contemporary of the great artist and breeder. *This seems to have taken place after the notorious Douglas cross in the 1850s, criticized by Tegetmeier (see p. 26).* At that time many crosses and experiments were taking place in the era of "Hen Fever".

Faults are white in the tail and on breast, absence of grey or black in hen's breast, and lack of size.

* There appear to be two distinct *standards* - one suggested by the APA (USA) and the same by the British standards, as well as an alternative British version.The coloured illustration by Harrison Weir follows the second choice and may be the correct one. White hackles are not compatible with the other dark colours.

**The position on the Silver Grey and Dark is puzzling and ambiguous. As noted under the description of the former (p. 57) the Silver Grey is regarded by many as a colour mutation of the Dark. However, illustrations around 1900 show that the Silver Grey was a more upright bird, without the very deep body of the Darks. Without doubting that they are bred from the Darks, the difference in shape and the purity of colour tends to suggest that a cross was introduced, such as a Grey Old English Game, and then brought back into line with a further Dark cross, once the silver-grey colour had been established.

The Old Kent Fowl
Harrison Weir – note the similarity to the Dorking

Silver Grey Dorking Hen
A prizewinner around 1900; note the carriage is not as low as present-day birds.

Red Dorkings

The Red Dorking is a beautiful breed, following the traditional Black Red pattern. They are said to have existed on records for around 400 years (Harrison Weir) and appear to have been kept pure, not being affected by the Dark variety cross (Edward Brown).

The male follows the traditional Black Red pattern: Black breast and tail and blue-black wing bar. The neck hackle is supposed to be a "glossy red", but in a painting by Harrison Weir this is shown as a Red which is darker on the edge and tends to be orangy in the centre (viewed from the side); the saddle hackle is a similar colour; the back is a deep red (burgundy) and the wing bay is orangy red.

The female has a reddy-brown body with a hackle a more golden colour, striped with black. The tail and primaries are black or very dark brown. The body feathers are tipped with black in the form of a spangle.

This is thought to be nearest to the Dorking of Roman times. Its comb tends to be smaller than the Darks or Silver Greys.

Silver Grey Dorkings

The Silver Greys are basically black (or dark) and white with a mixture of other colours. The male has a black breast, tail and lower parts, with the hackle, wing bows and shoulders white (with no markings or yellowy tinges). Wing **secondaries** white outer part and black inner; **primaries** black with white edge on outer web.

The female should be a delicate mottled grey on top together with a salmon-red breast which fades as it gets lower. The colour should be a nice soft shade which is free from mossiness or brownish tinges. The neck should be silvery white with a narrow stripe of black. This colour is regarded by many as the most beautiful. Pencilling in darker grey on the feathers should follow the outer line on each feather and not go across it.

These are very popular being very attractive. They were bred from the Darks, being very similar to that colour, but lighter- silver being the striking colour. Mr O E Cresswell introduced them by selecting the most silvery of the Darks and breeding them together to stabilize the colour (J Pettipher, *Poultry World Annual*, 1922)*.

Since the comb tends to go over a little, Other things being equal, the best combed birds should be the winners.

As noted in the section on numbers, the variety is the most popular and represents about half of all Dorkings kept in Britain.

* See earlier Footnote (page 55) on an additional possibility.

Red Dorking

Black Breasted Silver Grey Dorkings

Faults in Silver Greys include lack of size, white in tail or on breast of cock, red or brown top feathers in females and any deviation from the standard colours.

White Dorkings

The Whites should be white only free from any straw tinge. There are records of this colour dating back to 1815 or earlier. The rose comb should have a definite 'leader' in the manner of the Hamburgh, though not as prominent.

With the cherry red comb and face and pure white plumage this ranks as one of the most handsome of the white varieties. The body feathering is fairly close which makes them appear smaller than the standard Dark.

The variety, as painted by Harrison Weir about 1902, were more upright and had shorter bodies than the other main varieties. However, the Whites painted by Diane M Jacky in the *American Standards of Perfection* do have bodies which are long and low and which are typical Dorking shapes. It would seem therefore that the pair illustrated by Harrison Weir, *as a first impression*, were not typical of the variety, although they were owned by O E Cresswell a leading breeder of the time. However, those painted by Ludlow, owned by Miss Fairhurst, and reproduced in Lewis Wright's work *The Illustrated Book of Poultry*, were also rather upright, compared with the other colours portrayed. Since this pre-dated the Harrison Weir painting, being produced around 1880, we must conclude that the earlier types of Whites were different from the Darks and Light Greys, which came later anyway. The early illustrations from Lewis, given earlier, also corroborate this view. However, the very large square frame was a feature from early times so it does seem that it is the carriage which has varied, being upright on some varieties, for a period and then more boat-like later.

Undoubtedly, the rosecomb, with its long leader on the cock, almost helmet-like, makes the bird very attractive.

Variations in Standard Requirements (British)

The **Colour** requirement is very important in the Silver Grey (24 per cent of marks), but between 12 and 15 in the other varieties; **Size** is of vital importance in the Dark (28 per cent). **Type** carries 20 per cent in the Dark, Cuckoo and White and 12 per cent in Red and Silver Grey. In all varieties the **feet** account for 8 points.

White Dorkings painted by Harrison Weir
As noted in the text, this presentation of the shape and carriage is not in
accordance with today's *standard.*

Silver Grey Dorking Cock around 1900

Silver Grey Dorking Cock
Modern type: Courtesy Andrew Oatey, Past Chairman, Dorking Club

Faults

The faults relate to wrong colour legs or number of toes; lack of size – Darks are largest followed by Silver Greys and then Reds; white in breast which is black; Yellow or straw in white colour; incorrect type of comb; any deformities. Physical defects on comb and legs, including twisted toes are major faults.

The USA *standard* stipulates that ear lobes more than one third white should disqualify.

DORKING BANTAMS

The American Bantam Association recognizes five varieties:

> **Cuckoo (rose combed);**
> **Dark (rose combed);**
> **Dark (single combed);**
> **Silver Grey (single combed);**
> **White (rose combed).**

The British *standards* suggest the same colours as for large fowl, but in practice the breed is rarely seen in bantam form. Entwisle *(ibid)* noted that Silver Grey bantams were available, but had disappeared in the 1880s. This colour has been revived, but is not seen very often. The other varieties are extremely rare. It is great credit to the Americans that they continue to foster the five varieties.

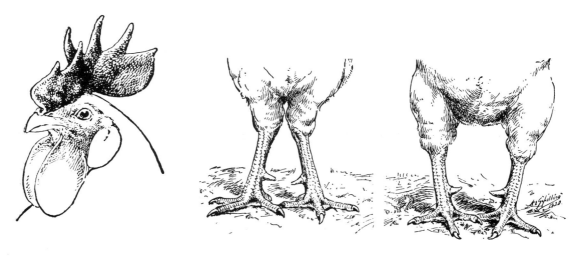

Faulty Comb   **Knock-kneed**   **Bow-legged**
Fish-tailed comb

Possible Physical Faults

SIX

THE EVOLUTION OF THE BREEDS WITH NOTES ON MANAGEMENT

Types of Breeds

The Sussex and Dorkings are farmyard poultry which have existed in the southern part of England for hundreds of years. Accordingly, their natural environment is out in the open, on free range, foraging for food, and enjoying the life of laying and putting on flesh. They are not likely to thrive well in close confinement, where the space is restricted and where they cannot be kept busy.

The Sussex, particularly the Light variety, can be expected to lay up to 200 eggs per annum, about 150 being the norm. Some varieties lay more, but if the breed is to be dual purpose the temptation to turn them into layers must be resisted. Some strains in the past have laid **very small** eggs and such birds should not be used for breeding.

Dorkings are not good layers and therefore how many eggs will be laid depends on the strain, but 100 per annum is possibly a reasonable average.

The weights for British Dorkings are 10 to 14 lb (4.5 to 6.4 kilos) for mature males and about 10 lb. for the female (4.5 K). It must be appreciated that they vary in size, dependent on the variety. When colours are listed separately (USA) they follow this sort of pattern:

White (lbs) 6 hen; 7.5 cock
Dark   7 hen; 9 cock
Silver Grey 7 hen; 9 cock.

In practice, the heavier varieties can reach over 6.50 kilos so the standard weights are simply a guide. Heavy weights are expected in Dorkings.

Sussex weights are expected to be in the region of 7 lb for females and 9 lb. for mature males. Again, some variation may be found between the different varieties. The need to retain a breed which is broad in breast is essential. That the breed is very hardy is evidenced by the fact that it has been bred for generations on the grey clay of the Weald of Sussex, a point made forcibly by Edward Brown (ibid). On this evidence it is therefore more adaptable than the Dorking which prefers a loamy or chalky soil. However, it should be clear that all breeds of fowl prefer a well drained soil, especially the heavy breeds. Muddy runs are a source of infection and no hen can be expected to produce under such conditions; the Dorking, being quite heavy and having short legs is at a disadvantage in adverse conditions.

The Development

There is little doubt that the Sussex-type fowl have been in existence for hundreds of years and they were the birds kept for table and laying. The recognition of separate breeds came with the poultry shows, but before that time poultry were an important part of the rural economy. Moreover, the market dictated which types should be kept; from early times there has been a preference for white skin and legs. Eggs were a secondary consideration although cottagers used to take fowl indoors at night to encourage the hens to lay.

The movement towards recognizing separate breeds started after about 1840 and the first show was organized by the London Zoological Society. It provided for Dorkings, Surrey fowl, **Old Sussex or Kent fowls**, Hamburghs, Malays & Asians, Polands, Bantams, and Spanish. This fact provides clear evidence that such fowl existed, alongside the Dorking.

Other shows were then established, including the Birmingham and Crystal Palace (1868) and "Dairy Show". In these early days the number of entries topped 3,000 (in 1889 at the Crystal Palace there were 3,487 entries). In these early shows the table fowl were also represented. However, in 1870 the Crystal Palace organizers had turned to plumage and condition of the exhibits so the movement towards the recognition of separate breeds was now established.

A fine Silver Grey Dorking Cock
Champion in 1923/4 for A J Major from his famous Stud

Champion Dark Dorking Cockerel
Breeder, T Briden, a major fancier, who had been showing for more than 50
years and was still showing at 90 years of age.

Early Exhibits

Poultry shows became the concern of royalty, landowners and other people of property or high rank. The winning birds fetched high prices. It was reported the the Countess of Dartmouth's prize winning birds, priced at 3 guineas, were actually sold for £9 – a very large sum for the year of 1869. Queen Victoria gave the shows her support and under the Royal patronage they flourished.

The first official **standards** were issued in Britain in 1864, but were found to have no authority when the Poultry Club was discontinued. Amended *standards* were issued by the re-formed Poultry Club of Great Britain (reformed 1877) in 1886; these were based on the work of Lewis Wright and others. In the USA *standards* were also developed in 1873 and issued the following year in book form. These were similar to the British *standards*, but gave a total of 100 points for perfection; the British *standards* had given 15 points which proved too inflexible.

It was against this background of great activity and enthusiasm for pure breeds of poultry that the "new" breed, the Sussex, was recognized in 1903. The breed was there, but following the fashion for new varieties the breed was crossed with the Asian type fowl, such as Brahmas, which had arrived around 1850 and new colours started to be created. These had to be transformed into the specification for Sussex so it was no small task for the many varieties to become recognized in the *standards*. There had been crosses earlier, particularly with Old English Game, but the new development was a positive attempt by enthusiasts to create as many varieties as possible.

Many breeders were responsible for the tremendous developments which took place and some of these are noted in the text. The Sussex Club also made up for lost time, catering for the enthusiasm which heralded the new varieties. It still remains strong and active.

Amongst the breeders A J Falkenstein deserves special mention. He was responsible for many advances made, including the the introduction of the White Sussex. In addition, he guaranteed classes at shows, thus encouraging the fanciers to exhibit their birds. His many wins at shows* included First and Best in Show at the Dairy show, and Olympia (1923) with Speckled Sussex and Light Sussex,

---

The Feathered World, 7th March, 1924, which includes full details as well as photographs of four winners on the front cover.

including a medal for the best Sussex. The photograph of the winning Light Sussex shows a pullet with well marked hackle – at a time when the norm were 'washed out' looking hackles. Indeed, his birds were far ahead of all others being shown at the time.

Sex Linkage in Sussex Chicks

The 'Gold' (Reds) and 'Silver' (Lights) provided the sex linkage in the chicks. The chicks show the opposite colour to the parents so a Rhode Island Red male with a Light Sussex hen will produce Red females and Light Males.

Sussex Bantams

The bantam came from different sources. The Light, the most popular, appear to have been developed from outcrossing the Columbian Wyandotte bantam to a large Light Sussex; It was this approach that developed the correct type of bantam which was a miniature of the large.

In terms of precedent, the position is uncertain; both Speckled and White were being developed from the early 1920s. Some state that the Speckled came first, but the *Poultry Year Book* for 1927 comes out in favour of the Light. Although all the colours of the Large can appear, there is a tendency for the colours seen to be Light, Silver, Speckled and White. Reds, Browns and Buffs are not as popular, but the position could change, depending on the fashion of the time; this is often dictated by a new winning strain appearing on the scene.

EVOLUTION -- SUSSEX FOWL
HISTORY

Established as a farmyard fowl for hundreds of years as Kent or Sussex fowl.

In July 1903 a Sussex Club was formed and the breed became standardized. In the USA this recognition came in 1914 for Speckled and Red and for the Light variety in 1929.

Initial Breeds (Pre-1903)

1. **Speckled**
2. **Red** – an overall, deep red colour with a striped hackle.
3. **Light** – Light Brahmas were used to create the colour.

New Varieties

4. **1908-9: Brown** – this is the normal Black Red type and may contain Old English Game blood.
5. **1918: Buff** – created by crossing the Buff Orpington with Light Sussex. The Buff Orpington had been produced by crosses which included Dorking.
6. **1925: White*** – a bird which was regarded as an excellent egg layer (175 recorded), but did not really 'catch on', possibly because it was not a typical Sussex colour in the hackle.
7. **1960s: Silver** – a modern creation which has not become well established, although very attractive.

The breed has been used as a basis for sex linkage breeding.

The dates are an indication of the approximate time of introduction as a variety, but should not be regarded as being rigid.

* A F Falkenstein showed this colour in 1926 and won prizes. See *Feathered World* for 15th October, 1926, for photographs of winning birds.

BANTAMS: These appeared much later than the Large fowl from around 1926. According to the *Poultry Year Book,* 1927, Light Sussex were being bred (1926), but in an imperfect condition. Almost simultaneously, the Speckled appeared; others were then developed in the immediate pre-1930 period, the Silver being much later. In the USA the APA recognized Light, Red, and Speckled only in 1960, although the American Bantam Association gave recognition earlier.

Silver Grey Dorking in 1893 drawn by Ludlow.

Note the difference in size, shape and carriage. Was Ludlow depicting the perfection sought but not yet achieved. Whites were not subjected to a size-increasing cross so they remained a different *type*, even today.

Dorkings in the 1860s from a Show Catalogue

This old print leaves much to be desired, but it does show the upright shape of the early birds. It is useful to compare the Whites on page 60, which are similar.

Development of the Dorking

As shown earlier, there is positive evidence that a fowl of the Dorking type has been around for near on 2,000 years. There are gaps in our knowledge on a number of matters:

1. **Were they always the deep bodied breed now standardized.**
2. **What was the original colour or colours.**

The Evidence Available

As shown in the earlier text, there are differences of opinion on what constitutes the early Dorkings and how the ideal matches up to the expectations.

A great deal of weight is carried by the pictorial records available and Ludlow the Victorian artist drew idealistic birds which he saw as the ideals. Unfortunately, he was often years ahead of reality so his drawings portrayed birds which came later.

According to Joseph Pettipher*, who remembered Dorkings from his boyhood, the breed was different 40 years before he was writing; ie, about 1880. However, this also happens to be the era of the Ludlow pictures and, therefore, their value should be treated with some reservation. Indeed, they are similar to the birds found today and no doubt the artist was instrumental in getting fanciers to aim for the deeper bird with the short legs.

Other evidence confirms this view. Around 1860 an engraving was completed for inclusion in the Birmingham Show Catalogue. Moreover, Joseph Pettipher* confirms that the type depicted in the engraving were the kind in existence at the time. They were, he states, "especially fine layers .... they were better foragers than the modern Darks and Silvers". Moreover, it will be seen, they do not have the very short legs which later became a craze.

In fact, the evidence provided by the engraving indicates a type of bird not much different from robust Old English Game. These are clearly active birds, foraging in a meadow for food.

An illustration of a prizewinning White cock which won in 1900 is also included in the Pettipher article; it is also a more upright type of bird. Mr Pettipher lamented the reduction in numbers of the Whites which had been very popular.

---

* *The Poultry World Annual*, 1922, p.183

EVOLUTION -- DORKING FOWL
HISTORY

Said to have come with the Romans around AD 47; therefore in Britain around 1,950 years. Only Old English Game may have a longer history. Many features have remained the same, including the fifth toe which is a distinguishing feature of the breed.

Admitted to British standards in 1865 for the breeds established. In the USA Whites, Silver Greys and Coloureds (Darks) were standardized in 1874.

1. 1815: White – one of the original colours and once very popular.

2. Pre-1850: Cuckoo or Barred – may have come from a cross with the American Dominique, but are out of favour **at present.**

1850s: or later: Dark – modified with a cross with an Asian breed to increase size and bone for show purposes.May also have been modified by a cross with the White and with Partridge Cochins.

1850s: Silver Grey – Created by selection of "silvery" birds and bred together by O E Cresswell a noted breeder.

1850: Red – a Black Red type fowl of the original Dorking pattern, not influenced by the Dark cross. Double mating was practised for a time leading to unpopularity.

The dates are an indication of the approximate time of introduction as a variety, but should not be regarded as being rigid.

The 1920s

The 1920 era saw great strides in the quality of the show Dorking. Unfortunately, like today, although excellent birds were around, they were not all being shown. One prominent writer, C A House suggested it was the lethargy of those who were running the Dorking Club. He had this to state for the 1921 show year:*

> **DORKINGS: Taking the breeds one naturally thinks first of the Dorking. A true Britisher, not many years since held in high esteem, not only for its beauty, but by reason of its utilitarian properties. It was England's best and greatest table breed. Thus it is difficult to understand why it has not made progress, but actually lost ground. At the three great shows of the year Dorking fanciers have not pulled their weight. The Dairy and Palace Dorkings were but as ghosts of those which have gone before, whilst at Birmingham the whole section was cancelled. There is a Dorking Club. What is it doing to stay the slump? So far as I can see and hear, nothing. A real live, energetic club is needed, unless the Dorking is to pass right away from our ken and be no more known. Old breeders have dropped out and no new ones come to take their place. Messrs Major, Aitkenhead, Mechie, Mason, Smyth and Proctor of the old brigade have shown us some splendid birds. But where are the newcomers? The Dorking Club needs to rouse itself and boom the breed.**

This was blunt criticism and possibly very harsh words, but such was the poultry fancy in those days, and more effort was needed to keep the fancy moving, when all around there was the stirring of revolutionary methods to replace the conventional poultry farming methods and, eventually, the neglect of the fine, standard bred birds.

NOTES ON SOME COLOURS
Red Dorkings

This handsome variety was kept by the Hamlin family for more than 100 years* and gave very good results. Yet for various reasons as early as 1914 it was in short supply. The possible reasons have been summarized by Joseph Pettipher*, a prominent breeder, as follows:

---

*The Poultry World Annual, 1922

1. When a standard was compiled breeders resorted to double mating to get the correct colours for the males and females and there was obviously something amiss with the standards that this had to be done to produce winners.

2. The size was inferior to the Darks and Silver Greys and, since bulk won prizes, the Red could not compete. The fact that the other colours had achieved bulk by becoming coarse, as observed by Tegetmeier and cited earlier, was immaterial.

Fortunately the present position is improving. On a visit to Andrew Sheppy in Somerset he reported very good progress with Red Dorkings. These were of a good type, foraged well and were good layers.

White Dorkings

As noted earlier, this variety is now very scarce. It tends to be more upright than the Darks and Silver Greys and not as heavy. This appears to be the case even today, although earlier, according to Lewis Wright, a large size was bred by a Mr John Martin as follows: Dark Cock X White Hen = Cuckoo. Cuckoo X Original Whites = Whites of much larger size. A 12lb. cock was bred, but after Lady Holmesdale (owner?) retired the stock was sold.

Dark & Silver Greys

The Darks were created into very large, bulky birds with deep bodies. This occurred from a cross in the 1850s. They have stayed larger than the early, traditional colours. The Silver Greys were produced from the lighter coloured birds bred by the Darks.

Cuckoo

The barred variety appear to be near extinction which is a great pity. The Cuckoo colour is attractive and needs no washing for the shows except the legs and face. It could be re-created by crossing with one of the existing varieties and a barred breed, such as the Scots Dumpy. An illustration of a *Cuckoo Sussex* is given on page 53.

POSSIBLE MANAGEMENT APPROACHES

There are many systems available for keeping poultry:

1.   Free Range

"Free Range" means the birds have full and free access to the outside, leaving and returning as they think fit. It is the Natural method which has many advantages and is regarded by many as being more humane than the other methods.

There are also disadvantages including the cost of land and possible loss of production in inclement weather.

A modified practical definition is considered later in this chapter.

2.   Restricted Free Range

Birds may be kept in feed units on grass or in pens, but with less land than full free range. For those with limited space this is possibly the best compromise, but has its limitations especially on the numbers which may be kept.

3.   Semi-Intensive
(including straw-yard,barn and aviary systems)

The semi-intensive system means that the birds have access to a grass run, but may be kept indoors when the weather is inclement. In addition, the amount of space available in the outside run is less than free range.

A modification is the farm-yard or straw-yard system, whereby poultry are allowed to roam around an enclosed yard which is littered with straw.

4.   Intensive Systems

These involve keeping many birds in a relatively small space. They may be distinguished by reference to the system of management:

(a) regular cleaning and replacement of litter; e.g. shavings, peat moss, but the birds are kept in crowded conditions.

(b) *deep litter* system, when a very thick layer of shavings is put into the shed and kept for 6 months or longer without being cleaned out.

(c) *battery system* which entails keeping birds in cages and having food and water provided quite automatically.

SPECIFICATIONS OF CAGES (Not recommended for Sussex or Dorkings)

The cages should comply with specified standards laid down by the regulations of the country concerned e.g. EEC regulations would apply to the countries in the Community. Birds confined in too small a space, or too many birds per cage can result in lost production as well as unhealthy hens. Bones become brittle, feathers are worn and birds become pale and lacking vitality.

Essentials are as follows:
1.   Reasonable capital cost per bird
2.   Large enough for birds to turn around
3.   Bars designed so as to give maximum access to food and water for all occupants and yet not catch or rub feathers.
4.   A monitoring system to be able to watch over birds on a regular basis

Light Sussex on Free Range

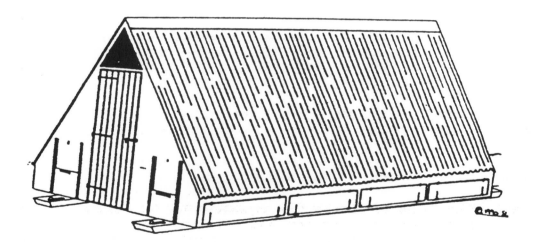

A Typical Free Range Shed on Skids

Early Light Sussex (1913)
Note the indistinct hackle markings of this early specimen (Lord Rothschild)

Brown Sussex Cockerel (1914)
Bred by J Ade

UNACCEPTABLE SYSTEM

On purely moral grounds it can be argued that close confinement is unacceptable, but on economic grounds (and until the general public will pay the extra cost for eggs or meat) the cage system
will prevail. The further away from Free Range we get the more un-
desirable the method. Battery cages, even under the regulations
which require more space and perches, are still far away from a
satisfactory standard.

Selection of Appropriate System*

The above systems may be adopted in their entirety or in some
form of combination e.g. free range for most times, but semi-intensive during the winter. Practical considerations are as follows:

1. Public Opinion

In recent years there has been a wave of feeling which is in opposition to
intensive systems or any methods which appear to restrain birds or over-
crowds them. Free range eggs may be sold at a higher price which helps to
offset the increased costs.

2. Capital Costs

A fully intensive house must be properly insulated and have special ventilation (usually fans). In addition, the cages, plumbing, automatic feeding
system, controlled lighting and other requirements all add to the very high
capital costs.

Free range systems are cheaper to install, but the labour costs
of feeding and management are higher.

3. Land Availability

Free range requires considerable land and, therefore, when large numbers
of birds are to be kept a farm is essential. Imagine the numbers achieved in
recent years and the land required! Holdings with 1 million birds have been
kept and this is only possible with the battery system.

Opinions differ on the space required for the pure system of free-range
poultry management. It seems certain that not more than 100 birds per acre
should be kept. The semi-intensive system may allow 300 birds per acre or,
with clever management, even more. However, it will be appreciated that any
attempt at overcrowding could lead to severe problems (discussed later).

---

*The coverage here is for those who wish to keep birds in considerable numbers; a
garden set-up would not require such a complex analysis; a small shed and run
would suffice for six hens and a cockerel. See *Garden Poultry Keeping*, J Batty

Light Sussex on a Small Scale

Sussex Broody Hen & Chicks
Sussex and Dorkings make excellent mothers

4. *Type of Land*

Land which becomes waterlogged and muddy is not ideal for poultry farming. Heavy breeds do not like too much mud and clay and it is said that the Dorkings are susceptible to health problems unless the soil is well drained. Apparently, they can withstand cold, but not excessive dampness.   On the other hand, dry, sandy scrub–land will not supply luscious green grass.   The latter is excellent food for birds and, in effect, is free.   Accordingly, its use would be maximised.

Very hot open areas are not conducive to maximum egg production. Trees or hedgerows may provide some shade. The siting of the houses will also affect the exposure to the weather.

Some breeds are more suitable than others for heavy soils and these should be selected with care.

5. *Access to Services*

Poultry require a regular flow of clean, pure water.   Accordingly, some form of piped system is essential.   Hose pipes can be used but there is a limit to the size of range which can be watered.   The problems of freezing–up can also be serious.

The foodstuffs, grit, etc. can be transported by tractor and trailer or on a four wheel vehicle.

Lighting is vital and power is desirable so again provision of this service should be considered.

Practical   Considerations

Bearing the above factors in mind it is useful to summarise some of the matters to be examined:

1.   Domestic Housing

Adequate housing for the poultry farmer and his family will be essential. Adjacent to the house should be outbuildings for the following:

(a) **food storage and mixing room;**

(b) **egg storage;**

(c) **gate–sales shop;**

(d) **incubation room (if required)**

2.   Access to Range

Full access to the range is a vital requirement. Hilly, undulating terrain should be avoided not only because of the difficulties of reaching the poultry houses, but also the inherent problems of security from foxes and thieves.

3. Ease of Partitioning for Field Rotation

As will be shown later, for many reasons it is desirable to rest each area to allow the grass to grow and to avoid infestation with disease carrying bacterias. Careful planning will repay itself many times over.

4. Privacy for Birds

Birds should be kept free from disturbance.

A MODIFIED DEFINITION OF FREE RANGE

Free access to a large area such as a field is the recognised definition of "free range". A population density of 50 to 100 birds per acre gives a guide to what is required. Assuming 100 birds per acre and allowing for a rotation system with changes every 6 months, 20 acres will be required per 1000 birds. For obvious reasons the **pure form** of free range may not be very profitable.

Instead, a *modified* type of free range may be necessary. Essentially the requirement is access to fresh air and a plentiful supply of natural foods without the fouling of the grounds. A great deal can be done to provide the necessary **ingredients** of free range.

This approach may suit the large type of Dorking which in their present form may not be able to cope with the rigours of full free range.

A Barn System – ideal for Sussex or Dorkings

The fresh air is no problem so the remainder must be provided in a variety of ways; for example:

1.   *Access to grass,* with a regular change over of birds to fresh pasture, thus allowing the grass to grow again.
2.   *The fold system,* moving the arks across the field on a regular basis.
3.   *Pens/aviaries/barns* in which supplements are regularly given by the addition of grass clippings, weeds, leaves and other foundation material.

All these enable birds to enjoy considerable freedom, to scratch and pick up green stuff, grit, grubs and other essentials. Above all, poultry must be kept interested so that they are constantly engaged finding food and enjoying it. Happy birds are productive birds.

The main features of these methods are now considered.

SMALL OR LARGE ?

A fundamental problem with free range is how big is the operation to reach. If relatively small with, say, 100 layers, then problems are not usually serious. Once the intention is to keep 1000 birds **and upwards** the difficulties multiply.

For the **small to medium size** type of operation with one or two fields available the free-range poultry keeping should be able to avoid all the excesses likely to cause problems. These are as follows:

1.   Overcrowding
2.   Sour ground
3   Disease becoming established in the ground so that each generation of birds has a high rate of mortality or poor production
4.   Disturbances due to behaviour of birds; fighting, overlapping of territories and the inevitable establishment of the "pecking order".

Overcrowding

Signs of overcrowding will be reflected in the ground becoming sour and the grass disappearing – usually in large patches, around and near the poultry houses. Once denuded there is great difficulty in getting the grass to grow. Instead of having natural surroundings to keep them occupied the birds are left to mope around or to stray

Sussex Arks – for keeping in small teams

Range Shelter
This method is cheap to produce and is ideal for the summer months.

further and further away with the inherent dangers of being killed by dogs, foxes or traffic.

Sites which are very exposed – a large open field – will tend to suffer from denuding of the grass, especially in summer. Some form of sprinkler system will overcome the problem provided the density of stocking is reasonable. With too many birds per acre nothing can stop the effects of wear and tear on the land.

Accordingly, a shaded spot is better with the sheds and large patches of the grass area being out of the direct rays of the sun. It is for this reason that many orchards have been used for keeping free range poultry. The hens can scratch under the fruit trees and will clear the area of insect pests. In addition, they will keep the grass short and eat any apples or pears which fall from the trees. Obviously though there is a limit to the number of birds which can be kept and the trees may make access to poultry houses quite difficult. For a small number of birds the system is ideal.

Overcrowding leads to stress in poultry. If too many are together or in small houses, but in near proximity, bullying and feather pecking will result with a loss in productivity. Moreover, the poor producers may not be detected with a lowering of the average per flock.

Sour Ground

The poultry farmer is faced with a dilemma. He must run birds on the land to the maximum possible extent, thus making the most of his investment and manuring the land to the full, yet he has to observe strict rules of good stock management and hygiene or within two or three years he will suffer quite serious problems.

Steps to be taken to avoid the effects of over intensive stocking are:

1. Move the sheds and the flocks to new ground each year. This is the safest way. However, it does represent a great deal of trouble. A more easily managed system would be to have duplicate housing and after two years to sell off the stock leaving the sheds available for a year for disinfecting, creosoting, etc. and then to restock.

Sheds with wheels or on skids can help if moves are to be made with the poultry houses.

2. Pay special attention to removal of manure and to installing methods of keeping faeces separate so the hens do not have to tread in it.

3. Inspect stock regularly and pick them up to check if they are producing. Handling and carrying out simple tests can eliminate the wasters.

4. Watch out for watery eyes, runny droppings, ruffled feathers, fish eyes and other signs of being out of condition.

5. Test eggs and meat of birds at regular intervals to make sure quality is maintained.

6. Watch for bullying and any malpractices such as egg eating.

FREE RANGE PROBLEMS

Psychologically, free range poultry keeping will always appear better than any other system. Fresh air, open spaces, natural food and freedom should lead to healthier birds and, therefore, better eggs or meat. No matter what scientists or poultry farmers state, the idea that *natural is best* will always prevail.

In an attempt to show there can be serious disadvantages it is necessary to consider some of the main problems which are as follows:

1. Productivity

Because of the climatic differences and the advent of the moult around 70 per cent production is in the Spring/Summer period and the remaining 30 per cent in the Autumn/Winter period.

Sussex are generally good Winter layers and with selection Dorkings could be reasonable, but in both cases the utility, all-round aspects should not be overlooked. The impact of the weather will reduce egg production, but can be maximized with proper management.

There is also the creation of a special environment and related requirements such as a full allocation of food, complete monitoring of production and the selection of a temperature which maximises egg production and keeps food costs down. Remember, in a cold Winter on free range, a bird will have to eat more to keep warm so production suffers. With the cage system there is no loss because of this fact; the birds are kept warm in an artificial environment..

2. Egg Quality

An argument for free range systems is that eggs are better quality. In fact, scientists have tried to show that there is no difference in **chemical content**, but who will believe this fact when comparing the rich taste of the freshly laid free range egg and the egg from a battery hen !

Analysed into its constituent parts an egg has the following ingredients:

	A %	B %
Water	74	65
Fat	10	10
Protein	13	11
Shell	Excluded	12
Undetermined		1
Ash	1	

Note: **A** = Free Range   **B** = Battery

The differences reflect different sources of information and obviously the methods used would affect the result. Rounding-up of figures has affected the accuracy to the total of 100 per cent.

What was found was that there was no noticeable difference between those eggs from free range and other systems and battery cages. Provided the food was properly mixed and balanced even the egg colour was similar.

3. Health of Birds

In modern times discoveries have been made which show that hens kept in cages develop brittle bones which may break easily. There is also a serious problem from disease, particularly salmonella, which has affected the acceptability of eggs as food.

Complacency, lack of controls, keeping very large flocks, absence of fresh air and many other factors have been blamed. Fortunately, the danger has been found and the alarm raised. Steps have been taken to avoid outbreaks of disease, and to give larger cages and alternative systems to allow each hen more space.

What should also be remembered is that free range can also be subject to disease, which may wipe out complete flocks. Therefore, hygiene and being run on "clean" ground is essential. Food fed to birds is excreted all around and comes with its potential disease, including coccidiosis and worms.

Each pullet will excrete around 200 lb. of fresh droppings each year so imagine the output from 1000 birds on a field. This manure contains about 1.5 per cent nitrogen and essentially will make the grass grow rich and green. Accordingly, if birds are transferred every six months and the ground allowed to "rest", possibly being limed, then the manure can do much good. However, if birds are kept on for long periods without rotation, the ground becomes sour and disease carrying, with the resultant deterioration in the health of the hens.

FULL FREE RANGE REQUIREMENTS

As noted earlier, for full range to apply it is essential to have a field on which suitable poultry houses are sited. The hens are let out each day and closed up each evening. They thus have access to a maximum amount of grass which is a valuable source of food and enriches the colour of the yolk to a deep yellow colour.

Security

The poultry houses are usually sited near the dwelling house so the farmer can keep the birds under observation. Opinions differ on how much fencing is necesary. Possibilities are:

1. No special fencing, but place the poultry houses well away from public roads so that birds do not stray and get killed or stolen.

A hedge, barbed/wire/netting or electric fence may be quite adequate. Generally houses are separated by about 50 metres so that each flock identifies with a specific shed and with training will go back into it for food and for roosting.

2. Wire netting partitions which allow each flock to be kept separate.

There can be a gate to give access and obviously provided the netting is high enough the birds will not mix. Where cocks are to be kept there should be adequate protection to avoid fighting. However, much depends on the breed. A pugnacious cock like an old English Game must have boards or corrugated sheets between the pens, but other cocks, such as Sussex, Dorkings or Rhode Island Reds will live quite happily together.

Free Range Layouts

Need for Males

If the purpose is to produce eggs or table birds, there is no need to keep any males whatsoever. However, for continuity, so as to be able to produce chicks from the best layers, it may be necessary to have one pen for breeding purposes.

Taken to the ultimate, hens should be "trap-nested" and a record kept of each egg laid. In this way it is possible to know which are the best layers and then, breeding from a cock, **also bred from a top layer,** the breeding pen should produce top layers.

For table birds those with broad breasts and excellent conversion properties (turning food into meat), should be the ones selected for breeding. Breeds like Indian Game become quite large and plump, but the growth is slow so crossing with another breed such as Light Sussex will give speedier growth. When crossed with Rhode Island Reds the sexes can be distinguished by the colour of the chicks. If Light Sussex cockerels are crossed with RI hens the chicks will be pullets a dark shade of buff (Gold) and cockerels cream (Silver); this is excellent for those who wish to specialize in providing day old cockerels for fattening.

Generally speaking around twelve females to one male **(10 to 1)*** is the correct ratio for breeding purposes. It follows, therefore, that the breeding pen should not be too large. If ten females are used, capable of laying 200 eggs each, this gives a potential hatching of 2000 which, allowing for wastage, is probably a chick potential of around 1700 (a loss of 15 per cent). For most purposes this kind of replacement may be quite adequate.

Against having a policy of hatching and rearing replacements is the danger of disease. Some poultry farmers specialise in producing pullets and obviously this may be an alternative approach. Once replacements are needed, they are bought in to keep production to a maximum.

If this approach is to be adopted then great care should be taken to select a breeder who is known to produce first class birds. Remember too that the hybrid strains developed over the last 50 years were produced for the specific purpose of battery or other intensive management systems. They have not been bred for free

---

* For very selective breeding much lower ratios may be followed ; eg, heavy breeds 5 to 1; exhibition fowl 2 to 1.

Indian Game Hen   **Old English Game Hen**

Wyandotte Hen

Useful Crosses
Crossed with Sussex or Dorking will provide excellent table birds.

range and, therefore, their potential may be suspect. How can we be sure of how such birds will react in conditions which are quite unlike those for which they were developed. It is rather like taking a greenhouse plant outside and hoping it will do just as well. As many gardeners will know this is a very unlikely occurrence.

Selected Crossing For Table

The usefulness of recognition through colour can be very importantl; if a Silver male is crossed with Gold female the progeny will be all **males gold** and **females silver.** If Silver females are crossed with Gold males the true sex linkage occurs (the Mendelian law); however, such pullets lose the sex linkage effect every alternate year.*

In Sussex there is the Light Sussex (Silver) and Red (Gold) which can be mated with suitable other breeds to give the sexlinkage.

On cross breeding many crosses have been suggested to produce birds for the table:

1. Indian Game X Light Sussex

The effect is greater weight with the retention of the white flesh. If better fertility is sought the second cross would be Indian Game X Light Sussex **X** Light Sussex.

2. Rhode Island Red X Sussex

As noted this is a sex link cross.

3. Sussex X White Wyandotte

The **Dorking** may also be used in a similar way, thus giving the white flesh and extra size. However, as noted, some strains of Dorking are slow to mature so more work would be needed to get the birds to the desired level of productiviity.

---

*Those wishing to study the subject further are advised to refer to books on the discoveries of Gregor Mendel; the works by Professor R C Punnet are very relevant.

Light Sussex of Good Type
Alert, bold eye, clearly a good layer

Young Sussex   **Head of Poor Performer**
Not making the grade   **Poor head, sunken, dull eye**

Keep only the Best

CONCLUSIONS

From what has been stated it should be apparent that both breeds have much to offer to the poultry keeper who wishes to keep birds on a small scale or as a business. These breeds are excellent table birds and the Sussex is a very commendable layer. For free range or semi-intensive, such as the Barn method or Aviary system, they are very suitable and, once the laying season is over, or when selected for fattening, they can be sold as top quality table birds which command premium prices.

On the exhibition side these breeds should be regarded as utility as well as show birds and should be viewed as such. Sheer size, with its attendent coarseness should not be the aim.

The Sussex bantams are also good layers and are an interesting and worthwhile breed to keep, offering a challenge to produce the correct Sussex markings. In Light Sussex there is strong competition so those in the winners can know that they are breeding along the correct lines. With Dorkings more effort is needed to bring the breed into prominence; only by increasing the numbers kept and offering incentives to fanciers will the breed emerge from obscurilty and improve. At present the bantams are not truly Dorkings so more effort is needed to improve the quality.

Despite the crosses which have been made the Sussex and Dorkings have many common characteristics which still exist today. They were developed from the needs of the farmer, the yeomen of England, who tilled the land, fattened poultry, sold eggs and depended on the activities pursued to earn a living. They were clearly related, being differentiated only by geographical location. The Kent fowl, Surrey fowl, Dorkings, and Sussex fowl were from the same family tree and the major difference – the fifth toe – was the main deviation. Even then there were many reports of Sussex with the extra toe and "Surrey fowl" without the appendage.

There is need for more positive efforts for breeders of both breeds, but especially the Dorking fraternity, to encourage more active movement into keeping them on free range. More education of the general public and poultry farmers is needed to overthrow the pre-eminence of the hybrid fowl which is not really suitable for free range anyway. Distribution of leaflets at shows and more publicity is needed or these ancient, useful breeds will disappear. Both breeds have active clubs, but tend to be known only to the fancier who has already been converted. The Poultry Club and the "Federation" should also do much more to make known the merits of these fine breeds.

The aviculturists (cage and aviary enthusiasts) put the poultry fanciers to shame. If a visit is made to a national cage bird show the turnout in terms of exhibits and fanciers, as well as the general public, the enthusiasm is very obvious. Moreover, the organizers make sure that the event is national news. This in itself makes for more breeders and enthusiasts. Yet on their relative merits the poultry breeds are much more useful, supplying eggs and meat to cover the costs. This is not intended to decry the keeping of birds for pleasure because it is an excellent pastime, but more should be done to encourage poultry keeping.

Early White Sussex (1923)
Bred by A J Falkenstein: note the shape is quite different from the Orpington and the
feathering is not too fluffy. See pages vii and 66.

POULTRY BREED CLUBS

Poultry fanciers and farmers may benefit greatly from membership of poultry bodies linked with their breeds. Some of these are listed below.

The Dorking Club
Sec. Mrs V Roberts
Heather Bank
Hillings, Menston,
Ilkley,
West Yorks, LS29 6AU

The Sussex Club
Sec. Mr M N Raisey
Exbury
Ahford Hill Rd
Headley, Newbury
Berks RG15 8AB

The Scottish Sussex Club
Sec. Mrs R Aitken
Hillberry
Dunnotter
Stonehaven,
Kincardinshire, AB3 2XB

The Rare Poultry Society
Sec. Mr R J Billson
Alexandra Cottage
8, St Thomas's Rd
Great Glenn
Leicestershire   LE8 0EG

The Poultry Club of Great Britain*
General Secretary: Mr M Clarke
30 Grosvenor Rd
Frampton
Boston
Lincs. PE20 1DB

* Covers all breeds and looks after the interests of the Fancy.

INDEX